TWENTIETH-CENTURY BESTIARY

a SCIENTIFIC AMERICAN book

SIMON AND SCHUSTER NEW YORK

PUBLISHED BY SIMON AND SCHUSTER, INC.
ROCKEFELLER CENTER, 630 FIFTH AVENUE
NEW YORK 20, N. Y.

FIFTH PRINTING
MANUFACTURED IN THE UNITED STATES OF AMERICA
PRINTED BY MURRAY PRINTING COMPANY
LIBRARY OF CONGRESS CATALOG CARD NUMBER: 55-12532

Previously Titled
FIRST BOOK OF ANIMALS

TABLE OF CONTENTS

INTRODUCTION ix

1. THE BALANCE OF NATURE

I. THE SPIDER AND THE WASP
by Alexander Petrunkevitch 3

II. SEA LAMPREY AND LAKE TROUT
by Vernon C. Applegate and James W. Moffett 9

As an example of balance, a certain spider invariably submits to the lethal advances of a particular wasp, though it can and often does kill any other kind of wasp. An instance of imbalance is the depredation of the trout of the Great Lakes by a jawless ocean fish that slipped in via the Welland Canal.

2. MATING

I. THE COURTSHIP OF ANIMALS *by N. Tinbergen* 19

II. THE CURIOUS BEHAVIOR OF THE STICKLEBACK *by N. Tinbergen* 26

III. THE HOME LIFE OF THE SWIFT
by David and Elisabeth Lack 35

In the varied and stylized rituals by which matings are established, there are many gambits and displays that suggest threat and aggression; the drive to mate must surmount the impulse to fight or flee. When he succeeds with his elaborate designs, the male stickleback assumes the role of nurse. The swifts take turns.

3. THE SOCIAL INSECTS

I. THE LANGUAGE OF THE BEES
by August Krogh 47

II. THE ARMY ANT
by T. C. Schneirla and Gerard Piel 54

III. THE TERMITE AND THE CELL
by Martin Lüscher 68

Insect societies show that adaptation can be achieved by the interaction

as well as the constitution of individuals. Foraging workers do a precision dance that tells other bees where to find nectar and pollen. Stereotyped army ants conduct their martial maneuvers by virtue of a propensity to commit social suicide. From its stock of undifferentiated larvae, a termite colony rears a constantly balanced hierarchy of specialized members.

4. ORIGIN OF SPECIES

I. DARWIN'S FINCHES *by David Lack* 77

II. THE END OF THE MOAS *by Edward S. Deevey, Jr.* 85

On the Galapagos Islands, where there were no other birds, a single species of finch evolved, in anatomy and behavior, into a wide variety of types, from seed-eaters to woodpeckers. In New Zealand, where there were no mammals, the wingless (and almost brainless) moas filled the vacant mammalian niches, evolving even a kind of avian giraffe.

5. PHYSIOLOGICAL ENGINEERING

I. THE METABOLISM OF HUMMINGBIRDS *by Oliver P. Pearson* 93

II. SHREWS *by Oliver P. Pearson* 100

III. THE DESERT RAT *by Knut and Bodil Schmidt-Nielsen* 109

Life's immense capacity for adaptation is demonstrated by its response to extreme conditions. One extreme is size: to maintain the heat of their tiny systems hummingbirds and shrews are furnished with ultra-high speed metabolisms. Another is lack of water: the desert rat's kidneys conserve the water it extracts from its dry provender.

6. FLIGHT AND NAVIGATION

I. BIRD AERODYNAMICS *by John H. Storer* 117

II. BIRDS AS FLYING MACHINES *by Carl Welty* 126

III. THE NAVIGATON OF BIRDS *by Donald R. Griffin* 135

IV. SONAR IN BATS *by Donald R. Griffin* 147

V. SONAR IN BIRDS *by Donald R. Griffin* 156

We have learned about birds from airplanes, not vice versa. They have slots and flaps as well as airfoils and propellers, and their airframes have exceedingly efficient weight-strength ratios. Bats and at least one kind of bird fly in the dark by echo-ranging. Progress in navigation is not yet sufficiently advanced to explain long-range homing and migration flights.

7. INSECTS IN THE LABORATORY

For some researches insects are more useful than guinea pigs. Delicate surgery on the glandular systems of caterpillars and roaches uncovers clues to endocrine function in man. The pattern of a spider web affords a way to distinguish and measure the effects of various drugs.

8. THE PROPER STUDY OF MANKIND

The nervous systems of higher animals provide models for the study of psychological and emotional processes in man. Neurosis can be induced in experimental animals at will by simple conditioning. The indefatigable monkey supports the Einstein dictum that "there exists a passion for understanding." The infant chimpanzee is smarter than a baby until the latter learns to talk.

INTRODUCTION

The reader has here in hand a twentieth-century bestiary. It is a sampling of the curious and wonderful inventions of life that have always intrigued the human imagination, itself the most wonderful and curious of life's inventions. Most of the creatures that abound in these pages have been encountered before by the reader, in nature or in books. In this book they are the subjects of observation and experiment by science. As will be seen, the scientist is attracted to his subject by the same questions that excite the nature lover—and the nature faker—to the speculations that surround the animal kingdom with its marvelous and dubious literature. Under scientific investigation, it turns out, these very questions lead straight to some of our most valid and useful insights into the ways and workings of life.

Almost all the chapters in this book were written by scientists closely associated with the work reported. They were addressed to the 130,000 subscribers and newsstand buyers who make up the diverse audience of the magazine SCIENTIFIC AMERICAN, *in which the chapters were first published as articles. Accordingly, they are written in nontechnical English prose to the interest and understanding of the general reader.*

The first several sections of the book are concerned with the behavior of animals. Like teeth, wings and body temperature, behavior is an adaptive device, fashioned under the pressures of natural selection, which secures the survival and perpetuation of species. In his account of the macabre relationship of a certain wasp and spider, Alexander Petrunkevitch shows how the behavior of hunter and hunted may be nicely adjusted to secure the survival of both. The sea lamprey provides an instance of imbalance, where the works of man have brought in from the oceans a primitive jawless monster whose predations have all but completely destroyed the long established trout population of our Great Lakes. Study of this creature's habits, happily, promises to bring it under control.

Perpetuation, as distinguished from survival, gives us some of our most engaging instances of animal behavior. Analyzing a variety of complex rituals into their component themes, N. Tinbergen concludes that courtship is close to conflict. The triumph of behavioral evolution is, of course, social behavior. All three of the social insects are represented in this book. Under scientific observation, they throw little light on human society, but they suggest the extraordinary capacity of life to orchestrate its elaborate systems out of simple units. The reduction of the concerted activity of the swarm to explanation in terms of the rudimentary equipment of its individual members yields much more fascinating stories than the exponents of the pathetic fallacy have ever told.

It was the finches of the Galapagos Islands that stirred in Darwin's imagination the first glimmering of his historic explanation for the origin of species. David Lack shows how a single species of finch emigrating to these once birdless islands proceeded to diversify in anatomy and behavior to fill all the niches in the environment that might have been occupied by other birds. At the opposite extreme is Edward Deevey's mournful chronicle of the moas. Evolving in an environment that offered no mammalian competition, these wingless birds assumed even the role of giraffes. It was an experiment that failed, for they are no more.

The hummingbird and the shrew, the tiniest of birds and mammals, demonstrate a general law of life: that consumption of energy must go up as size goes down. Oliver Pearson shows that they generate heat and activity at a rate per ounce that makes our living look like slow motion. How the desert rat manages to survive in such waterless locales as Death Valley provides another instance of the range of physiological engineering. As the Schmidt-Nielsens explain, it is a matter of kidney design.

Now that we have learned to fly we are beginning to understand how birds do it and to appreciate how much we could have learned from them about aerodynamics had we known what questions to ask. With our present sophistication, it is plain to see that birds are equipped with airfoils, flaps, slots and propellers. Similarly, with the invention of radar and sonar, scientists have discovered that bats and at least one species of birds employ the same echo-ranging principle for flying in the dark. The long-distance navigation of birds on their homing and migration flights, however, remains a mystery that must perhaps await analogous advances in the aerial navigation of men.

The last sections of the book take the animals into the laboratory for investigation of some broader questions than are suggested by the animals themselves. The universality of life makes man kin to the humblest of his fellow creatures. The processes of the human endocrine system may be approached, therefore, by investigation of the hormones that regulate the metamorphosis and growth of the caterpillar and wood roach. In the derangement of the pattern of a spider web, there is found a quantitative measure of the effect of drugs on men. The conditioned reflex in the sheep offers a way to study neurosis in people. Our kinship with the primates is, of course, a more familiar sensation. The studies reported here, however, bring it more uncomfortably home that the differences between men and animals are not so much of kind as of degree.

THE EDITORS *

PART 1 THE BALANCE OF NATURE

I. THE SPIDER AND THE WASP

by Alexander Petrunkevitch

The world's leading authority on the spider, Alexander Petrunkevitch retired as professor of zoology at Yale University in 1945. But he has by no means retired from research. Recently he spent six months in the museums of England and the Continent studying the fossil arachnida and is now engaged in research on those entombed in amber.

II. SEA LAMPREY AND LAKE TROUT

by Vernon C. Applegate and James W. Moffett

As zoologists with the U. S. Fish and Wildlife Service responsible for conditions in the Great Lakes, the authors have a particular stake in the subject of this article. Vernon C. Applegate is a New Yorker who did his undergraduate and graduate work at the University of Michigan; he began his study of the lamprey problem for the Conservation Department of the state of Michigan in 1945. James W. Moffett was born in American Fork, Utah, and in his youth worked on ranches and in mines and sawmills. He, too, took a Ph.D. in zoology at the University of Michigan. Applegate is director of the Fish and Wildlife research laboratory in the Great Lakes, and Moffett is chief of investigation.

THE SPIDER AND THE WASP

by Alexander Petrunkevitch

In the feeding and safeguarding of their progeny insects and spiders exhibit some interesting analogies to reasoning and some crass examples of blind instinct. The case I propose to describe here is that of the tarantula spiders and their archenemy, the digger wasps of the genus Pepsis. It is a classic example of what looks like intelligence pitted against instinct—a strange situation in which the victim, though fully able to defend itself, submits unwittingly to its destruction.

Most tarantulas live in the tropics, but several species occur in the temperate zone and a few are common in the southern U. S. Some varieties are large and have powerful fangs with which they can inflict a deep wound. These formidable looking spiders do not, however, attack man; you can hold one in your hand, if you are gentle, without being bitten. Their bite is dangerous only to insects and small mammals such as mice; for a man it is no worse than a hornet's sting.

Tarantulas customarily live in deep cylindrical burrows, from which they emerge at dusk and into which they retire at dawn. Mature males wander about after dark in search of females and occasionally stray into houses. After mating, the male dies in a few weeks, but a female lives much longer and can mate several years in succession. In a Paris museum is a tropical specimen which is said to have been living in captivity for 25 years.

A fertilized female tarantula lays from 200 to 400 eggs at a time; thus it is possible for a single tarantula to produce several thousand young. She takes no care of them beyond weaving a cocoon of silk to enclose the eggs. After they hatch, the young walk away, find convenient places in which to dig their burrows and spend the rest of their lives in solitude. The eyesight of tarantulas is poor, being limited to a sensing of change in the intensity of light and to the perception of moving objects. They apparently have little or no sense of hearing, for a hungry tarantula will pay no attention to a loudly chirping cricket placed in its cage unless the insect happens to touch one of its legs.

But all spiders, and especially hairy ones, have an extremely delicate sense of touch. Laboratory experiments prove that tarantulas can distinguish three types of touch: pressure against the body wall, stroking of the body hair and riffling of certain very fine hairs on the legs called trichobothria. Pressure against the body, by a finger or the end of a pencil, causes the tarantula to move off slowly for a short distance. The touch excites no defensive response unless the approach is from above where the spider can see the motion, in which case it rises on its hind legs, lifts its front legs, opens its fangs and holds this threatening posture as long as the object continues to move.

The entire body of a tarantula, especially its legs, is thickly clothed with hair. Some of it is short and woolly, some long and stiff. Touching this body hair produces one of two distinct reactions. When the spider is hungry, it responds with an immediate and swift attack. At the touch of a cricket's antennae the tarantula seizes the insect so swiftly that a motion picture taken at the rate of 64 frames per second shows only the result and not the process of capture. But when the spider is not hungry, the stimulation of its hairs merely causes it to shake the touched limb. An insect can walk under its hairy belly unharmed.

The trichobothria, very fine hairs growing from disklike membranes on the legs, are sensitive only to air movement. A light breeze makes them vibrate slowly without disturbing the common hair. When one blows gently on the trichobothria, the tarantula reacts with a quick jerk of its four front legs. If the front and hind legs are stimulated at the same time, the spider makes a sudden jump. This reaction is quite independent of the state of its appetite.

These three tactile responses—to pressure on the body wall, to moving of the common hair and to flexing of the trichobothria—are so different from one another that there is no possibility of confusing them. They serve the tarantula adequately for most of its needs and enable it to avoid most annoyances and dangers. But they fail the spider completely when it meets its deadly enemy, the digger wasp Pepsis.

These solitary wasps are beautiful and formidable creatures. Most species are either a deep shiny blue all over, or deep blue with rusty wings. The largest have a wing span of about four inches. They live on nectar. When excited, they give off a pungent odor—a warning that they are ready to attack. The sting is much worse than that of a bee or common wasp, and the pain and swelling last longer. In the adult stage the wasp lives only a few months. The female produces but a few eggs, one at a time at intervals of two or three days. For each egg the mother must provide one adult tarantula, alive but paralyzed. The mother wasp attaches the egg to the paralyzed spider's abdomen. Upon hatching from the egg, the larva is many hundreds of times smaller than its living but helpless victim. It eats no other food and drinks no water. By the time it has finished its single gargantuan meal and become ready for wasphood, nothing remains of the tarantula but its indigestible chitinous skeleton.

The mother wasp goes tarantula-hunting when the egg in her ovary is almost ready to be laid. Flying low over the ground late on a sunny afternoon, the wasp looks for its victim or for the mouth of a tarantula burrow, a round hole edged by a bit of silk. The sex of the spider makes no difference, but the mother is highly discriminating as to species. Each species of Pepsis requires a certain species of tarantula, and the wasp will not attack the wrong species. In a cage with a tarantula which is not its normal prey the wasp avoids the spider, and is usually killed by it in the night.

Yet when a wasp finds the correct species, it is the other way about. To identify the species the wasp apparently must explore the spider with her antennae. The tarantula shows an amazing tolerance to this exploration. The wasp crawls under it and walks over it without evoking any hostile response. The molestation is so great and so persistent that the tarantula often rises on all eight legs, as if it were on stilts. It may stand this way for several minutes. Meanwhile the wasp, having satisfied itself that the victim is of the right species, moves off a few inches to dig the spider's grave. Working vigorously with legs and jaws, it excavates a hole 8 to 10 inches deep with a diameter slightly larger than the spider's girth. Now and again the wasp pops out of the hole to make sure that the spider is still there.

When the grave is finished, the wasp returns to the tarantula to complete her ghastly enterprise. First she feels it all over once more with her antennae. Then her behavior becomes more aggressive. She bends her abdomen, protruding her sting, and searches for the soft membrane at the point where the spider's leg joins its body—the only spot where she can penetrate the horny skeleton. From time to time, as the exasperated spider slowly shifts ground, the wasp turns on her back and slides along with the aid of her wings, trying to get under the tarantula for a shot at the vital spot. During all this maneuvering which can last for several minutes, the tarantula makes no move to save itself. Finally the wasp corners it against some obstruction and grasps one of its legs in her powerful jaws. Now at last the harassed spider tries a desperate but vain defense. The two contestants roll over and over on the ground. It is a terrifying sight and the outcome is always the same. The wasp finally manages to thrust her sting into the soft spot and holds it there for a few seconds while she pumps in the poison. Almost immediately the tarantula falls paralyzed on its back. Its legs stop twitching; its heart stops beating. Yet it is not dead, as is shown by the fact that if taken from the wasp it can be restored to some sensitivity by being kept in a moist chamber for several months.

After paralyzing the tarantula, the wasp cleans herself by dragging her body along the ground and rubbing her feet, sucks the drop of blood oozing from the wound in the spider's abdomen, then grabs a leg of the flabby, helpless animal in her jaws and drags it down to the bottom of the grave. She stays there for many minutes, sometimes for several hours, and what she does all that time in the dark we do not know. Eventually she lays her egg and attaches it to the side of the spider's abdomen with a sticky secretion. Then she emerges, fills the grave with soil carried bit by bit in her jaws, and finally tramples the ground all around to hide any trace of the grave from prowlers. Then she flies away, leaving her descendant safely started in life.

In all this the behavior of the wasp evidently is qualitatively different from that of the spider. The wasp acts like an intelligent animal. This is not to say that instinct plays no part or that she reasons as man does. But her actions are to the point; they are not automatic and can be modified to fit the situation. We do not know for certain how she identifies the tarantula—probably it is by some olfactory or chemo-tactile sense—but she does it purposefully and does not blindly tackle a wrong species.

On the other hand, the tarantula's behavior shows only confusion. Evidently the wasp's pawing gives it no pleasure, for it tries to move away. That the wasp is not simulating sexual stimulation is certain, because male and female tarantulas react in the same way to its advances. That the spider is not anesthetized by some odorless secretion is easily shown by blowing lightly at the tarantula and making it jump suddenly. What, then, makes the tarantula behave as stupidly as it does?

No clear, simple answer is available. Possibly the stimulation by the wasp's antennae is masked by a heavier pressure on the spider's body, so that it reacts as when prodded by a pencil. But the explanation may be much more complex. Initiative in attack is not in the nature of tarantulas; most species fight only when cornered so that escape is impossible. Their inherited patterns of behavior apparently prompt them to avoid problems rather than attack them. For example, spiders always weave their webs in three dimensions, and when a spider finds that there is insufficient space to attach certain threads in the third dimension, it leaves the place and seeks another, instead of finishing the web in a single plane. This urge to escape seems to arise under all circumstances, in all phases of life and to take the place of reasoning. For a spider to change the pattern of its web is as impossible as for an inexperienced man to build a bridge across a chasm obstructing his way.

In a way the instinctive urge to escape is not only easier but often more efficient than reasoning. The tarantula does exactly what is most efficient in all cases except in an encounter with a ruthless and determined attacker dependent for the existence of her own species on killing as many tarantulas as she can lay eggs. Perhaps in this case the spider follows its usual pattern of trying to escape, instead of seizing and killing the wasp, because it is not aware of its danger. In any case, the survival of the tarantula species as a whole is protected by the fact that the spider is much more fertile than the wasp.

SEA LAMPREY AND LAKE TROUT

by Vernon C. Applegate and James W. Moffett

FOR MORE THAN eighty years fishing in the Great Lakes has been a sizable industry and a popular recreation for fishermen of the U. S. and Canada. Each year it yields a commercial catch of more than 100 million pounds of choice food, to say nothing of the millions of pounds caught by sportsmen. The most prized fish, and the backbone of the fishing industry, has been the lake trout. In good years the trout catch amounted to more than 15 million pounds, worth nearly $8 million. But in the past fifteen years the Great Lakes trout has suffered a disaster. The U. S., preoccupied with more spectacular troubles on a global scale, has not paid a great deal of attention to this calamity in its own backyard, though it threatens to destroy an important industry and relaxation.

The trout catastrophe began in Lake Huron in 1939. The fish suddenly began to decline in numbers, and within fourteen years it had all but disappeared from that lake; the catch dropped from more than five million pounds a year to 344,000 pounds in 1953. The same fate began to overtake Lake Michigan's trout in 1946, and the catch there fell from more than five and a half million pounds to a mere 402 pounds in 1953. Now the slaughter has started in Lake Superior and has begun to cut sharply into its annual trout catch of four and a half million pounds.

Neither overfishing nor weather nor disease is responsible for the annihilation of the trout. The culprit is an eel-like fish known as the sea lamprey. It is a murderous animal efficiently equipped with tools for destroying fish much larger than itself. The lamprey has a sucker-like mouth, sharp teeth and a tongue as rough as a file. Attaching itself to its victim with its mouth, it rasps a hole in the fish's body and sucks the blood and body juices; it is assisted in this by a substance in its saliva, called lamphredin, which prevents coagulation of the blood and dissolves the torn flesh. The victim thrashes about violently but cannot shake off its parasite. The lamprey, a swift swimmer with excellent vision, makes easy prey of fishes, because they are not alarmed by it and tend to ignore it until it strikes. Once it has gained a hold, the lamprey hangs on until it is satiated or the victim dies. A full-grown lamprey may kill a delicate fish such as the trout in as little as four hours. When the victim is more hardy, or the lamprey small, the parasite may cling and feed on the fish for days or even weeks. In the laboratory large lampreys stick to their victims for an average of about forty hours if the fish survive that long.

The sea lamprey is a newcomer to the upper Great Lakes. It is a marine species which, like certain salmon, hatches in a freshwater stream, migrates to the ocean to spend its adult life, and then comes back to fresh water to spawn. In some places it has adjusted itself to spend its entire life cycle in fresh water, passing its adulthood in lakes instead of in the ocean. It is an old inhabitant, for example, of the St. Lawrence River and Lake Ontario. Until 1829 the Niagara Falls blocked it from migrating into the other Great Lakes. Then the building of the Welland Ship Canal provided a passage around the Falls to Lake Erie, but the lamprey seems to have been slow to take advantage of the route. No lamprey was seen in Lake Erie until 1921.

In Lake Erie the lamprey did not flourish; the waters were too warm and the spawning conditions poor. But by the late 1930s the destroyer had penetrated into the next of the Great Lakes,

Lake Huron. Fishermen's nets began to bring up trout and other fish with ugly wounds on their bodies. Sometimes the fish had lampreys still clinging to them. Lake Huron was a particularly favorable environment for the lampreys; they multiplied rapidly and made great inroads into the fish of that lake. Meanwhile they also spread through the Straits of Mackinac into Lake Michigan and increased meteorically there. Apparently further migration into Lake Superior was slowed by the locks and dams at the head of Saint Marys River, but the lampreys finally cleared that hurdle and are now well established in Superior.

The kill of trout by the lampreys was prodigious. Experiments in laboratory aquaria have shown that during its period of active feeding a lamprey kills a minimum of 20 pounds of fish. As many as 25,000 spawning lampreys have been trapped in a single northern Lake Huron stream in a year; simple arithmetic shows that this one group must have destroyed 500,000 pounds of fish.

Commercial fishing for trout in Lakes Huron and Michigan came to an end several years ago. As the trout gave out, the lampreys turned more and more to other fish—whitefish, suckers, walleyes and so forth. Today much of the fishing industry in the Great Lakes is in serious economic difficulty. If the Lake Superior trout go, the industry there probably will collapse. To try to save the trout and other fish, the U. S. Fish and Wildlife Service, the Great Lakes states and Canada have been carrying on research and testing measures against the lampreys. A treaty for joint action by the U. S. and Canada was signed on September 10, 1954, and awaits ratification.

As in any pest-control problem, we must find the vulnerable points in the life cycle of the animal to attack it effectively. The life cycle of the sea lamprey begins in the shallow riffles of a stream. Here it passes the major portion of its life as a blind, harmless larva. Of its approximately seven-year life span, a lamprey spends only the last eighteen months in the lakes as a parasite. At the end of that time it goes back to the stream to spawn and die. Let us follow the cycle in some detail from the spawning stage.

The old sea lampreys begin their migration up the tributaries of the Great Lakes to spawn in early spring, the time of migration in each lake depending on the water temperature. They congregate in bays and in the estuaries of rivers during late winter, and when the stream temperature rises above 40 degrees Fahrenheit they start moving upstream. They seek out streams with a gravel or sand bottom and a moderately strong current.

Normally the male starts building the nest; then he is joined by a female who helps in the construction. They clear a small area, picking up stones with their sucker-like mouths and piling them in a crescent-shaped mound on the downstream side of the nest. When the nest is finished and the temperature of the stream is warm enough (over 50 degrees F.), the spawning begins. The female extrudes a small number of eggs; the male at once fertilizes them, and the eggs are carried by the current to the gravel rim of the nest, where they lodge in the spaces among the stones. Then the female lays another batch of eggs and the process is repeated. The eggs accumulating in the nest rim are covered with sand and additional stones. The pair go on producing fertile eggs until they are spent—after anywhere from one to three days. Then both partners die within a matter of hours.

The female has deposited from 24,000 to 107,000 eggs; the average is about 61,500. Fortunately less than 1 per cent of these eggs will hatch out into larvae.

Hatching takes ten to twelve days. The hatched larvae remain buried in the sand and gravel until about the twentieth day. Then the tiny creatures, only about a quarter of an inch long and hardly thicker than a fine needle, emerge from the nest and drift downstream until they reach quiet waters. Here they dive for the bottom and each digs an individual burrow. This will be its home for about five years, unless erosion washes it away. Throughout its larval life the young lamprey is blind and harmless. It sucks food, mainly microscopic organisms, from the water passing the mouth of its burrow. A filtering apparatus in its throat keeps out debris and passes food organisms to its digestive tract.

After four years the larva undergoes a striking metamorphosis. It develops large, prominent eyes, a round mouth lined with horny teeth, a filelike tongue and enlarged fins. Its slim body becomes dark blue above and silvery white beneath. The new young lamprey, some four to seven inches long, may emerge from its mud flat when late fall rains raise the river level, but usually it waits until the spring breakup and flood. It drifts downstream to the big lake and begins its parasitic existence, living on the blood of fish. Feeding upon a succession of hosts, it grows very rapidly, attaining a final length of 12 to 24 inches.

The adult lamprey apparently has a great range of movement. Marked lampreys, released in the autumn at the northern tip of Lake Huron, were recovered throughout the length and breadth of the lake by the following spring. Several individuals had traveled nearly the entire length of the lake, a distance of over 200 miles. But details of the lampreys' movements in the lakes are scanty. There is some evidence that they migrate first to deep water, where they attack lake trout, chubs and other deep-water species. As the lampreys grow larger, they move shoreward and in the fall are found in relatively shallow water. It is at this time that attacks on whitefish, suckers and other shallow-water fish reach their maximum.

Toward the end of winter sexually maturing lampreys begin to assemble off the mouths of streams. During this waiting period tremendous internal changes occur. The sex glands expand enormously, while the digestive tract shrinks and the lamprey becomes incapable of feeding. From now on it will live only on its own tissues. Even its muscles, skin and eyes deteriorate. If the lamprey is delayed in reaching its spawning grounds, death may overtake it before it can spawn.

Plainly the most vulnerable times in the lamprey's life are its periods in the stream—as a larva or young migrant and later when it goes back to spawn. The vulnerability is enhanced by the fact that only about two hundred streams tributary to Lakes Huron, Michigan and Superior are suitable for spawning.

One attack on the lampreys has been to build mechanical weirs and traps and barrier dams to block their spawning runs. Although effective, these devices have numerous drawbacks. They are generally expensive to install and maintain; the weirs and traps must be cleared regularly. They may break down under flood conditions. The reproductive potential of the sea lamprey is so great that even a few escaping individuals can "seed" a stream sufficiently to maintain the population.

When the shortcomings of the mechanical barriers became evident, we turned to electricity. Linear arrays of electrodes were set up in the water to create electrical fields just strong enough to stop the movement of lampreys upstream to their spawning grounds. Using regular 110-volt alternating current, the electrical devices are more economical to construct and operate than purely mechanical structures. Unfortunately, however, the prevention of spawning, even if completely successful, will not show results for at least seven years. It will not kill off the generations of larvae already in the streams.

If we could destroy the larvae or the young downstream migrants, we might reduce the population substantially in less than two years. But so far no practicable means of achieving either objective has been found. Traps for capturing the downstream migrants do not work during the flood stages, when most migration occurs. A dam with an inclined-screen trap is effective, but it is expensive to build and requires continual attention. Furthermore, in many streams the topography precludes the use of this type of structure. Attempts were made to electrocute the young migrants with a simple system of electrodes in the stream, but these experiments were discontinued when it was discovered that young lampreys are extraordinarily resistant to electrical currents and the power required would be prohibitively costly. As for destroying the larvae, the problems become even more difficult. It was found that young American eels, a notably voracious species, would destroy lamprey larvae, but they kill desirable fish as well. So do most poisons. Recent investigations have, however, encouraged the hope that we may find chemicals which are toxic to lampreys and relatively harmless to other fish. Thousands of chemicals are being tested in an effort to discover a specific larvicide.

Notwithstanding the defects of the available control methods, the urgency of the Great Lakes fishing industry's plight has prompted us to apply some of them while better methods are being sought. Electromechanical barriers have been installed in forty-four tributaries of Lake Superior on the U. S. side and twenty-four more are under construction in Canada. Practically all the spawning streams in the U. S. part of the Lake Superior basin have been blocked. In Lakes Michigan and Huron of course it is too late to save the trout. But if the trout can be protected in Lake Superior, they will provide a supply of eggs for restocking Michigan and Huron when the sea lamprey has been brought under control.

Fortunately no other fish has usurped the environmental niche of the trout in the Great Lakes. The small fishes on which trout feed have increased to the point of overcrowding, and there will be an abundance of food for trout when they can return. Another encouraging factor is that lampreys apparently do not single out trout if there are larger fish around. Thus when effective control of lamprey spawning comes into sight, we can begin to plant lake trout with the hope that the lamprey can be exterminated before the young trout grow large enough to be attacked. This may reduce the time required to develop a breeding population of trout from eleven years to seven.

Complete eradication of sea lampreys from the Great Lakes above Niagara Falls is our objective. It may prove to be a long operation, as difficult as the campaign sometimes necessary to stamp out an agricultural or forest pest, but we are confident that we shall ultimately succeed.

PART 2 MATING

I. THE COURTSHIP OF ANIMALS
by N. Tinbergen

II. THE CURIOUS BEHAVIOR OF THE STICKLEBACK
by N. Tinbergen

Lecturer in animal behavior at Oxford University, N. Tinbergen has been a naturalist since boyhood days and has studied everything from birds to flowers. Since 1937 he has worked closely with the noted Austrian naturalist Konrad Lorenz. Tinbergen's lectures at the University of Leiden had long been famous; he was invited at the end of World War II to conduct the same sort of program at Oxford, where he now has many pupils. He is author of *The Herring Gull's World.*

III. THE HOME LIFE OF THE SWIFT
by David and Elisabeth Lack

Before her retirement to look after their two sons, Elisabeth and David Lack spelled each other at the task of monitoring the domestic affairs of the swift. David Lack is director of the Edward Grey Institute of Field Ornithology at Oxford and the author of some notable bird books, including *The Life of the Robin* and *Darwin's Finches,* the latter being the subject of a later chapter of this book. The Lacks were married in 1946, shortly after Mrs. Lack had left wartime service and joined the Institute's staff.

THE COURTSHIP OF ANIMALS

by N. Tinbergen

WHEN A GOLDEN PHEASANT cock displays his brilliant plumage before a hen, we are accustomed to say he is courting her. Just what this expression means when applied to a non-human animal is far from clear; the idea is so obviously anthropomorphic that zoologists have been reluctant to pursue it seriously by taking up the study of animals' so-called "courtship" activities. Yet these strange, often grotesque activities are there, like Mount Everest, and they have challenged some of us to explore them.

In contrast to such clearly motivated behavior as feeding or flight from predators, the courtship postures of animals are altogether puzzling, because it is difficult to see at first glance not only what circumstances cause them to occur but even what functions they serve. We may suppose that the male's display and activities stimulate the female to sexual co-operation, but even this elementary assumption has to be proved. And then we have to ask: Why does the female have to be stimulated in so elaborate a fashion, and what factors enter into the male's performance?

Among the famous students of animal courtship have been T. H. Huxley and F. C. Selous of England, J. Verwey of the Netherlands and, more recently, Konrad Lorenz of Austria. Encouraged by their work, I have, together with my associates J. van Iersel, M. Moynihan and D. Morris, studied the courtship of various animals for several years, and we believe we have discovered some highly interesting facts which may apply to many other animals besides the specific ones we have observed.

We started by experimentally checking the well-known "releaser" theory of Lorenz. This theory holds that many animals have evolved special organs whose only function is the presentation of specific stimuli to fellow members of the same species. Thus birds' songs often have the specific functions of attracting females and repelling males. The gaping mouths of songbird babies in the nest, according to this theory, prompt the parents to feed them. Lorenz suggested that the releasers included movements, calls, brightly colored structures and so on. The releaser theory goes back to Darwin's writings on sexual selection, but Lorenz described the functions of the releasers more exactly than Darwin could, and he united under one heading a wide variety of phenomena. His theory is the only attempt so far to define the survival value of structures such as the vocal organs of songbirds, and thus to indicate how selection can account for the evolution of such complicated organs. It is also an attempt to explain communication among socially co-operating animals. We have shown the application of the releaser theory to many kinds of communication among animals, and present here some examples.

That sounds commonly act as releasers is abundantly clear: one proof is the fact that animals respond to auditory signals, including imitations or recordings, with all other stimuli excluded. The strident screeching of locusts has been shown to act on the tympanic organs, and, through them, on the behavior of the recipients. So-called alarm signals of birds are another example: it is often possible to make a bird crouch or exhibit some other anti-predator response by imitating the alarm call of its species.

There is some evidence that odors act as releasers. The virgin females of many moths are known to attract males by specific scents. It has been shown that the female of the grayling butterfly does not co-operate in copulation if the male's scent organs on the forewings have been covered up.

As for visual releasers, an example is the typical mating posture of a willing female bird; among many birds, for instance, a male in sexual condition will mate not only with a female but also with another male or even with a stuffed or dead male, provided the latter is presented in the typical female posture. As another instance, the male grayling butterfly can be induced to pursue a dummy of almost any color, size or shape if the dummy is moved in a certain sexually inviting way. Again, the red patch on the lower mandible of the adult herring gull has been shown to release and direct food-begging behavior in the young. To take still another example, when the underside of a male three-spined stickleback fish turns red, it releases sexual behavior in the female.

We can conclude, then, that the releaser theory illuminates at least one aspect of courtship: the stimulation to sexual co-operation. Still, there is another side to the story. Every naturalist knows that these conspicuous displays must make their performers vulnerable to attack by predators. For this reason one might expect the releasers to be restricted to the bare minimum—just an occasional flash of bright color or a short outburst of calling, followed by an immediate reaction of the female. But that is not what happens. Courtship is usually a prolonged affair; the female's co-operation comes only hesitantly and after a period of hours, days or sometimes even weeks.

The English biologist Fraser Darling suggested as a possible explanation that the prolonged courtship might be necessary to stimulate the growth of internal organs indispensable for mating, such as the gonads and other endocrine glands. This may be true; the evidence is still meager. Our work suggests another reason, namely, that courtship serves not only to release sexual behavior in the partner but also to suppress contrary tendencies, that is, the tendencies to aggression or escape.

In many animals aggression and flight are just as important elements in reproductive behavior as the physical union itself. They serve the function of segregating the pairs, and thereby preventing overcrowding. The best-known example is the system of staking out a territory. The males of many species of birds and of other animals select a territory in the spring and drive other males of their species away from it. Conversely, and this is just as important, males still searching for a suitable place do not waste their time and energy in hopeless battles to take one already occupied. All animals have developed a delicate balance between the tendency to attack and the tendency to flee. The relative strength of these two tendencies, the size of the distance kept between males, the stimuli by which each animal recognizes its own species—all these differ from one species to another. The function of the segregation system also varies widely: it may be to reserve a special nesting site or to guarantee sufficient food for the brood. In general it seems that the system serves to ensure to each breeding pair something that is essential for success in breeding.

When one studies hostile behavior between animals of the same species in detail, it becomes clear that much of it consists of "threat displays" rather than actual fighting. The object is to scare intruders away. Often the overt threat movements or postures combine elements of both attack and escape tendencies. For instance, the stickleback fish and some birds alternate short dashes toward the opponent with quick retreats; the herring gull and related species alternately bristle in a posture of attack and cringe as if to escape. Often the antagonists busy themselves with irrelevant "displacement activities"; thus an excited male stickleback may suddenly start digging purposelessly in the sand (see next chapter). Herring gulls show displacement collecting of nest material in the same situation. These activities have an intimidating effect on the opponent.

Now when, armed with this knowledge, one returns to mating

behavior, one suddenly sees that much of the courtship of animals is very similar to their threat displays. In other words, if we are to judge by overt behavior (and on what else could we base our work?) we must assume that when male and female come together they are motivated not only by sexual attraction but also by attack and escape tendencies.

As an example let me give a brief sketch of what happens when gulls of the black-headed species form pairs at the beginning of the breeding season. The two sexes are very alike in color and in display, and aggressiveness is not an exclusively male attribute. An unmated male settles on a mating territory. He reacts to any other gull that happens to come near by uttering a "long call" and adopting an oblique posture. This will scare away a male, but it attracts females, and sooner or later one alights near him. Once she has alighted, both he and she suddenly adopt the "forward posture," with their heads ducked low and extended. Sometimes, in this position, they may perform a movement known as "choking." Finally, after one or a few seconds, the birds almost simultaneously adopt the "upright posture" and jerk their heads away from each other.

Now most of these movements take place in purely hostile clashes between neighboring males. They may utter the long call, adopt the forward posture and go through the choking and the upright posture. All these movements may alternate with actual flights; the motivation underlying them has been shown to be a mixture of the tendencies to attack and to escape. Their function is intimidation; in other words, they are true threat postures.

To those who have studied the reproductive behavior of various animals in natural surroundings it is not at all surprising that the male and female show signs of hostility. Despite the attraction between sexes, their close proximity to each other also evokes fear and aggressiveness. The spacing-out mechanism conflicts with the mating mechanism.

The final gesture in the courtship sequence—the partners' turning of their heads away from each other, or "head-flagging"—is different from the others: it is not a threat posture. Sometimes during a fight between two birds we see the same head-flagging by a bird which is obviously losing the battle but for some reason cannot get away, either because it is cornered, or because some other tendency makes it want to stay. This head-flagging has a peculiar effect on the attacker: as soon as the attacked bird turns its head away the attacker stops its assault, or at least tones it down considerably. However, he does not do so because he is intimidated; there is no sign of fear in his behavior. Head-flagging stops the attack because it is an "appeasement movement"—as if the victim were "turning the other cheek." The appeasement posture soothes the aggressor by removing the provocation, the attack-releasing stimulus. An appeasement posture is motivated by a mixture of the tendency to stay and the tendency to escape.

We are therefore led to conclude that in their courtship these gulls begin by threatening each other and end by appeasing each other with a soothing gesture. Their courtship sequence is obviously made up of three elements: sexual attraction draws the partners together, attack and escape tendencies make them adopt threat postures, and at the end increasing escape tendencies cause them to turn their heads away. After the head-flagging, one or both birds frequently fly off, only to return.

The black-headed gull is not an isolated case. We have learned that our courtship theory applies to many other birds (including various finches, tits, cormorants, gannets, ducks) and to animals of quite different groups, such as fish. The expression of the triple motivation is different in each case. For instance, the relative strengths of the attack and escape tendencies may be very different from those in the black-headed gull. Often the male is aggressive, the female timid. Also, the males of some species are much more aggressive than those of others. The male river bullhead, for instance, attacks the female, grabs her with his huge mouth and throws her into his burrow. The males of some finches, on the other hand, show very little aggressiveness; they are torn mainly between sexual attraction and fear.

Let us return to our starting question: Why is courtship so prolonged? A pair of black-headed gulls may repeat again and again the courtship sequence of approach, threat and appeasement. Often the female flees or the male flies off to attack another male before the sexual union is achieved. The partners repeatedly are reattracted to each other, however, and gradually the threat elements decrease in vigor and frequency, aggressiveness and fear die down and the purely sexual movements get the upper hand. How this comes about is not known in detail; the process is certainly different from one species to another. In the gulls it appears that hostility declines because the partners get used to each other as individuals. The sticklebacks do not learn to recognize individuals; it looks as if in their case the mere repetition and summation of sexual stimulation ultimately overrides fear and aggression.

It is still an open question whether this gradual change in the motivational situation is mediated by endocrine changes, such as growth of the gonads. Future research will have to settle this. Our theory, as very briefly outlined here, is but a first step in the unraveling of the complicated causal relationships underlying the puzzling but fascinating phenomena of courtship.

THE CURIOUS BEHAVIOR OF THE STICKLEBACK

by N. Tinbergen

When I was a young lecturer in zoology at the University of Leiden twenty years ago, I was asked to organize a laboratory course in animal behavior for undergraduates. In my quest for animals that could be used for such a purpose, I remembered the sticklebacks I had been accustomed as a boy to catch in the ditches near my home and to raise in a backyard aquarium. These former pets soon proved to be ideal laboratory animals. They are so tame that they submit unfrightened to laboratory experiments, for the stickleback, like the hedgehog, depends on its spines for protection and is little disturbed by handling. Furthermore, the stickleback turned out to be an excellent subject for studying innate behavior, which it displays in some remarkably dramatic and intriguing ways. We found it to be the most reliable of various experimental animals that we worked with (including newts, bees, water insects and birds), and it became the focus of a program of research in which we now use hundreds of sticklebacks each year. The stickleback today is also a popular subject in various other zoological laboratories in Europe, notably at the universities in Groningen and Oxford. To us this little fish is what the rat is to many American psychologists.

My collaborator J. van Iersel and I have concentrated on the stickleback's courtship and reproductive behavior. The sex life of the three-spined stickleback (*Gasterosteus aculeatus*) is a complicated pattern, purely instinctive and automatic, which can be observed and manipulated almost at will.

In nature sticklebacks mate in early spring in shallow fresh waters. The mating cycle follows an unvarying ritual, which can be seen equally well in the natural habitat or in our tanks. First each male leaves the school of fish and stakes out a territory for itself, from which it will drive any intruder, male or female. Then it builds a nest. It digs a shallow pit in the sand bottom, carrying the sand away mouthful by mouthful. When the depression is about two inches square, it piles in a heap of weeds, preferably thread algae, coats the material with a sticky substance from its kidneys and shapes the weedy mass into a mound with its snout. It then bores a tunnel in the mound by wriggling through it. The tunnel, slightly shorter than an adult fish, is the nest.

Having finished the nest, the male suddenly changes color. Its normally inconspicuous gray coloring had already begun to show a faint pink blush on the chin and a greenish gloss on the back and in the eyes. Now the pink becomes a bright red and the back turns a bluish white.

In this colorful, conspicuous dress the male at once begins to court females. They, in the meantime, have also become ready to mate: their bodies have grown shiny and bulky with 50 to 100 large eggs. Whenever a female enters the male's territory, he swims toward her in a series of zigzags—first a sideways turn away from her, then a quick movement toward her. After each advance the male stops for an instant and then performs another zigzag. This dance continues until the female takes notice and swims toward the male in a curious head-up posture. He then turns and swims rapidly toward the nest, and she follows. At the nest the male makes a series of rapid thrusts with his snout into the entrance. He turns on his side as he does so and raises his dorsal spines toward his mate. Thereupon, with a few strong tail beats, she enters the nest and rests there, her head sticking out from one end and her tail from the other. The male now prods her tail base with rhythmic thrusts, and this causes her to lay her eggs. The whole courtship and egg-laying ritual takes only about one minute. As soon as she has laid her eggs, the female slips out of the nest. The male then glides in quickly to fertilize the clutch. After that he chases the female away and goes looking for another partner.

One male may escort three, four or even five females through the nest, fertilizing each patch of eggs in turn. Then his mating impulse subsides, his color darkens and he grows increasingly hostile to females. Now he guards the nest from predators and "fans" water over the eggs with his breast fins to enrich their supply of oxygen and help them to hatch. For a day or so after the young emerge the father keeps the brood together, pursuing each straggler and bringing it back in his mouth. Soon the young sticklebacks become independent and associate with the young of other broods.

To get light on the behavior ot man, particularly his innate drives and conflicts, it is often helpful to study the elements of behavior in a simple animal. Here is a little fish that exhibits a complicated pattern of activities, all dependent on simple stimuli and drives. We have studied and analyzed its behavior by a large number of experiments, and have learned a good deal about why the stickleback behaves as it does.

Let us begin with the stimulus that causes one stickleback to attack another. Early in our work we noticed that a male patrolling its territory would attack a red-colored intruder much more aggressively than a fish of some other color. Even a red mail van passing our windows at a distance of 100 yards could make the males in the tank charge its glass side in that direction. To investigate the reactions to colors we made a number of rough models of sticklebacks and painted some of the dummies red, some pale silver, some green. We rigged them up on thin wires and presented them one by one to the males in the tank. We found that the red models were always more provoking than the others, though even the silvery or green intruders caused some hostility.

In much the same way we tested the influence of shape, size, type of body movement and other stimuli, relating them to specific behavior in nest building, courting, attack, zigzag, fanning and so on. We discovered, for example, that a male swollen with food was courted as if it were a female.

As our work proceeded, we saw that the effective stimuli differed from one reaction to another, even when two reactions were caused by the same object. Thus a female will follow a red model wherever it leads; she will even make frantic efforts to enter a nonexistent nest wherever the model is poked into the sand. Once she is in a real nest, she can be induced to spawn merely by prodding the base of her tail with a glass rod, even after she has seen the red fish that led her there removed. At one moment the male must give the visual signal of red; at the next, this stimulus is of no importance and only the tactile sensation counts. This observation led us to conclude that the stickleback responds simply to "sign stimuli," i.e., to a few characteristics of an object rather than to the object as a whole. A red fish or a red mail truck, a thrusting snout or a glass rod—it is the signal, not the object, that counts. A similar dependence on sign stimuli, which indicates the existence of special central nervous mechanisms, has been found in other species. It seems to be typical of innate behavior, and many social relationships in animals apparently are based on a system of signs.

Sticklebacks will respond to our stimuli only when they are in breeding condition. At other seasons they ignore the signs. This fact led us to investigate the internal factors that govern the fish. The obvious way to study such fluctuations is to measure the frequency and intensity of a response under standard stimulation. For some of these tests we used either uniform models or live fish confined in glass tubes so that we could control their movement.

To measure the parental drive we adopted the standard of the number of seconds spent in fanning a given number of eggs per time unit.

The stickleback's drives in the breeding sequence wax and wane in a series of cycles. Each drive runs its course in regular succession: first the male gets the urge to fight, then to build a nest, then to court a female, then to develop the brood. He will not start to build, even though material is available, until he has defended his territory for a while. Nor will he court until he has built the nest; females that approach him before the nest is finished are driven off or at best are greeted with a few zigzags. Within each cycle also there is a fixed rhythm and sequence; for example, if you fill up the pit the male has dug, he will dig one again before collecting nest material. After the pit has been filled several times, however, the fish will build the nest without completing the pit. The development of his inner drive overcomes outside interference.

It seems likely that the rise and fall of inner drives is controlled by hormonal changes, and we are now studying the effects on these drives of castrating and giving hormones to the males. One interesting finding so far is that castration abolishes the first phases of mating, but has no effect on the parental drive. A eunuch stickleback, when given a nest of eggs, ventilates it with abandon.

In any animal the innate drives themselves are only the elementary forces of behavior. It is the interaction among those drives, giving rise to conflicts, that shapes the animal's actual behavior, and we have devoted a major part of our work with the stickleback to this subject. It struck us, as it has often struck observers of other animals, that the belligerent male sticklebacks spent little time in actual fighting. Much of their hostility consists of display. The threat display of male sticklebacks is of two types. When two males meet at the border of their territories, they begin a series of attacks and retreats. Each takes the offensive in his own territory, and the duel seesaws back and forth across the border. Neither fish touches the other; the two dart back and forth as though attached by an invisible thread. This behavior demonstrates that the tendency to attack and the tendency to retreat are both aroused in each fish.

When the fight grows in vigor, however, the seesaw maneuver may suddenly change into something quite different. Each fish adopts an almost vertical head-down posture, turns its side to its opponent, raises its ventral spines and makes jerky movements with the whole body. Under crowded conditions, when territories are small and the fighting tendency is intense, both fish begin to dig into the sand, as if they were starting to build a nest! This observation at first astonished us. Digging is so irrelevant to the fighting stimulus that it seemed to overthrow all our ideas about the specific connection between sign and response. But it became less mysterious when we considered similar instances of incongruous behavior by other animals. Fighting starlings always preen themselves between bouts; in the midst of a fight roosters often peck at the ground as though feeding, and wading-birds assume a sleeping posture. Even a man, in situations of embarrassment, conflict or stress, will scratch himself behind the ear.

So it appears that the stickleback does not start digging because its nest-building drive is suddenly activated. Rather, the fish is engaging in what has been called a "displacement activity." Alternating between the urge to attack and to escape, neither of which it can carry out, it finally is driven by its tension to find an outlet in an irrelevant action.

A similar interaction of drives seems to motivate the male when he is courting. In the zigzag dance the movement away from the female is the purely sexual movement of leading; the movement toward her is an incipient attack. This duality can be proved by measuring the comparative intensity of the two drives in an individual male and relating it to his dance. Thus when the sex drive is strong (as measured by willingness to lead a standard female model) the zig component of the dance is pronounced and may shift to complete leading. When the fighting drive is strong (as measured by the number of bites aimed at a standard male model) the zag is more emphatic and may become a straightforward attack. A female evokes the double response because she provides sign stimuli for both aggression and sexuality. Every fish entering a male's territory evokes some degree of attack, and therefore even a big-bellied female must produce a hostile as well as a sexual response.

This complexity of drives continues when the fish have arrived at the nest. A close study of the movement by which the male indicates the entrance shows that it is very similar to fanning, at that moment an entirely irrelevant response. This fanning motion, we conclude, must be a displacement activity, caused by the fact that the male is not yet able to release his sex drive; he can ejaculate his sperm only after the female has laid her eggs. Even when the female has entered the nest, the male's drive is still frustrated. Before he can release it, he must stimulate her to spawn. The "quivering" motion with which he prods her is much like fanning. It, too, is a displacement activity and stops at the moment when the eggs are laid and the male can fertilize them. It is probable that the male's sex drive is frustrated not only by the absence of eggs but also by a strong conflict with the attack drive, which must be intense when a strange fish is so near the nest. This hostility is evident from the fact that the male raises his dorsal spines while exhibiting the nest to the female.

The ideas briefly outlined here seem to throw considerable light on the complicated and "irrelevant" activities typical of innate behavior in various animals. Of course these ideas have to be checked in more cases. This is now being done, particularly with fish and birds, and the results are encouraging.

I am often asked whether it is worth while to stick to one animal species for so long a time as we have been studying the stickleback. The question has two answers. I believe that one should not confine one's work entirely to a single species. No one who does can wholly avoid thinking that his animal is The Animal, the perfect representative of the whole animal kingdom. Yet the many years of work on the stickleback, tedious as much of it has been, have been highly rewarding. Without such prolonged study we could not have gained a general understanding of its entire behavior pattern. That, in turn, is essential for an insight into a number of important problems. For instance, the aggressive component in courtship could never have been detected by a study of courtship alone, but only by the simultaneous study of fighting and courtship. Displacement activities are important for an understanding of an animal's motivation. To recognize them, one must have studied the parts of the behavior from which they are "borrowed" as well as the drives which, when blocked, use them as outlets.

Concentration on the stickleback has also been instructive to us because it meant turning away for a while from the traditional laboratory animals. A stickleback is different from a rat. Its behavior is much more purely innate and much more rigid. Because of its relative simplicity, it shows some phenomena more clearly than the behavior of any mammal can. The dependence on sign stimuli, the specificity of motivation, the interaction between two types of motivation with the resulting displacement activities are some of these phenomena.

Yet we also study other animals, because only by comparison can we find out what is of general significance and what is a special case. One result that is now beginning to emerge from the stickleback experiments is the realization that mammals are in many ways a rather exceptional group, specializing in "plastic" behavior. The simpler and more rigid behavior found in our fish seems to be the rule in most of the animal kingdom. Once one is aware of this, and aware also of the affinity of mammals to the lower vertebrates, one expects to find an innate base beneath the plastic behavior of mammals.

Thus the study of conflicting drives in so low an animal as the stickleback may throw light on human conflicts and the nature of neuroses. The part played by hostility in courtship, a phenomenon found not only in sticklebacks but in several birds, may well have a real bearing on human sex life. Even those who measure the value of a science by its immediate application to human affairs can learn some important lessons from the study of this insignificant little fish.

THE HOME LIFE OF THE SWIFT

by David and Elisabeth Lack

THE OLD BOOKS on birds started with the eagle because he, by virtue of his strength and size, was king of the birds. But in the nineteenth century kings were tumbled from their thrones by black-coated republican intellectuals, and the bird books followed suit. The birds of prey were dismissed as primitive, and the crow and its relatives were honored as the most intelligent and social of birds. Ours is sometimes called the century of the common man, and the modern order of birds appropriately reaches its climax with the weaver finches, of which the most familiar is the humble and town-loving English sparrow. Perhaps now, in an age characterized by fast travel and intricate machines, it is time to select as pre-eminent that bird which excels where birds are most at home—in the air. For this honor the bird known as the swift is the strongest candidate.

The swift spends almost its entire life on the wing. Swifts gather all their food and nesting material in flight, they drink by skimming over the surface of still water, they mate in mid-air, they may even pass the night without roosting. They never set foot on the ground except when hurt; they nest and rest in holes in trees, cliffs or buildings. They are the most aerial of all birds.

The swift has wings that are long, thin and curved somewhat backwards, the shape best adapted to rapid flight. Still it can maneuver more skillfully than other long-winged birds. This is because the wing of the swift is mostly supported on the bones of its large "hand," leaving its relatively small upper arm free to act as a joint with which to rotate the wing as a whole. In most small birds the bones of the forearm, midarm and hand are about equal in length; on the upstroke the wing is folded at the wrist and the flight feathers are opened. In the swift the flight feathers are locked together, and the wing is as stiff as a paddle. On the upstroke its leading edge is turned backward. Only the hummingbird, which is related to the swift, flies in a similar fashion.

The aerial life of the swift has certain drawbacks. Swifts have such long wings and short legs that their takeoff from the ground is very slow. This limits their choice of nesting sites to places above the ground which have a clear drop to permit a rapid takeoff. Further, because swifts find all their food in the air, they are dependent on fine warm weather. Under cold, wet or windy conditions insects are scarce in the air and swifts have great difficulty in finding enough food.

It is therefore not surprising that nearly all the seventy species of swifts are tropical. Only two, the common swift of Europe and Asia and the chimney swift of North America, breed in the cool temperate zone, and even these stay just for the summer. In winter they retire to the tropics. Here we are concerned with the European bird, and the reader should bear in mind that the chimney swift and other species have rather different habits, particularly at the nest.

We started our observations of the swift in a quiet English village near Oxford, where the birds nested in the thatched roofs of cottages. Unhappily we could reach the nests only from the outside with the help of ladders, and so we made little headway. Later we received permission to study 20 pairs of swifts living 100 feet above the ground in the tower of our own Oxford University Museum of Zoology. In winter, while the swifts were in Africa, we substituted boxes for the ventilators in which they nested. We then built a platform inside the tower and set up ladders which gave access to it. When the swifts returned for the summer, they accepted the change without disturbance and our detailed studies began. We found the parents remarkably tame. This is probably because they normally nest in holes that are closed at the rear, and thus have evolved no response to an enemy coming at them from the rear. The birds soon got quite used to us and allowed us to take their eggs or young from them and put them back again without any fuss. Later we were even able to place bands on the parent birds, provided we did not lift them from the floor of the box.

Next winter we went a step further, taking out the wooden backs of the boxes and replacing them with glass. The tower was almost dark, the only light coming from the entrance holes of the boxes themselves. We could now sit in the half-darkness and watch the swifts from, if necessary, a range of a few inches. It was fascinating to study the birds at such close quarters, and to know that we were the first to observe many of their breeding habits. Indeed, it was hard to believe they were the same creatures that outside the tower could be seen dashing madly through the air.

The swifts arrive at the beginning of May and at once occupy their boxes. Banding shows that each swift normally pairs with its mate of the previous year, but, since the birds usually return on different days, they perhaps rejoin each other merely because they have come back to the same box as before. After pairing, however, they recognize each other. If a strange bird enters the box it is immediately attacked. Early in the season strange birds sometimes try to drive the owners from their boxes, and violent fights occur. Among most wild birds fighting takes the form of song and display without actual blows. But in the half-light of their holes swifts cannot use such refined methods. Instead they grip each other tightly with their sharp-pointed claws and peck each other with their beaks. Sometimes they remain locked together for as long as five hours, until one bird drags the other to the entrance of the nest and both fall out. The performance is less dangerous than it looks, for the birds nearly always grip each other by the legs, where they do no harm, and their beaks are so soft that the pecks are almost harmless!

Courtship, again because it happens in semidarkness, is simple compared with that of most other birds. The chief display is for each bird to preen the other on the throat and neck, the parts which a swift cannot reach for itself. This mutual preening is accompanied by a soft, high-pitched clucking. The birds also mate in the boxes, but despite much watching we saw them do so only occasionally. On the other hand, there are many reports of one swift diving on to the back of another in the air, both then descending with screams. It has long been disputed whether this aerial encounter is mating. We conclude that it is because it occurs only at the same season of the year (late May) and at the same times of day (around 8 A.M. and 6 P.M.) as mating in the boxes, and because the latter is uncommon. So far as is known, swifts are the only birds which mate in this fashion.

Because the swift collects the material for its nest from the air, it does so chiefly in windy weather. With its beak it catches feathers, leaves, straw, the aerial seeds of certain trees, flower petals, scraps of paper and other objects. Both male and female swifts collect this aerial flotsam, and, unlike most birds, they continue adding to the nest as they incubate their eggs. The nest material is cemented in place with saliva, as it is by other swift species. (The saliva of a cave-dwelling Oriental swift provides the basis for the well-known Chinese "bird's nest soup.")

The eggs are white, like those of other birds which nest in dark places. During the day one parent sits on the eggs while the other is out feeding, and later they change places. In fair weather, when insects are plentiful in the air, the bird that is out feeding quickly collects enough of them and may return in less than half an hour. In cold or windy weather it may have to hunt more diligently, and its mate may be left sitting for as long as five hours. If it is alone for a very long time, the sitting bird goes out to feed without waiting to be relieved, presumably because its need for food is so great. The eggs may then be left uncovered for several hours. Because this happens mostly in cold weather we wondered what might happen to the eggs, but to our surprise they hatched normally. No other bird which nests in cool regions leaves its eggs unincubated for such long periods without harm. Apparently evolution has adapted the swift's eggs to withstand cooling, and the same applies to the newly hatched and naked young. When we first found young birds cold and unattended, we thought the parents had deserted them, but it was merely that both parents were out hunting. Provided that enough food was found, the young came to no harm.

Both parents feed the young. Most insect-eating birds bring one or a few insects to their nestlings every few minutes, but the insects taken by the swift are so small, and the birds may have to travel so far to collect enough of them, that the interval between feedings is much longer. In good weather each parent returns about every three quarters of an hour; in poorer weather, only about once in three hours; in bad weather the interval is longer still. The feeding parent gradually collects a large number of insects, still alive but entangled in saliva, in the back of its throat. By the time a swift is ready to return to its young, its throat is so distended that it looks like a miniature pouter pigeon. A single ball of food weighs more than a gram and contains anywhere from 90 smallish insects to 800 very small ones. When the bird returns to the nest, the whole ball is passed to one of the nestlings, which may thus gulp down in one mouthful up to 10 per cent of its own weight in food. Only when the young are very small does the parent share the food among them.

We found that if we took a nestling from the box just after it had been fed, we could manipulate the food from its throat, and in this way we were able to analyze the insects collected by the parent. We learned that they included almost every type of insect to be found in the air except butterflies and most dragonflies, which are too large for the throat of a swift, and thrips and other minute forms, which are presumably too small to be seen by a swift on the wing. The swift of course does not fly at random with its mouth open, but uses its eyes and departs from its course if it sees an insect. It also searches in likely places. When the weather is good and the wind moderate, swifts like to cruise up and down the windward side of a row of trees bordering open ground. This is because insects are blown against the trees and then up, and so are concentrated there. In windy and wet weather, when few terrestrial insects rise into the air, swifts hunt over open water, because then May flies and other aquatic insects emerge.

We were able to measure the feeding efficiency of certain parent swifts we knew well. One bird was out of the box for 64 minutes, after which it brought back 1.7 grams of small insects for its young. Another collected 1.2 grams, in addition to anything it may have eaten itself, in 47 minutes. We reckoned that on a fine day each pair came back with about 50 grams of insects. When the birds cannot find food because of bad weather, the young may go for several hours, and sometimes for a day or more, with nothing to eat. This is most unusual for small birds. In wet weather small insect-eating birds such as flycatchers and swallows can often find insects under trees, but the swift has such long, thin wings that, good flier though it is, it cannot maneuver in these enclosed spaces. Nor does it alight to feed. Thus the young swift has evolved several remarkable adaptations to help it withstand starvation.

The nestlings of the songbirds that have been studied thus far increase steadily in weight as they get older. If food is short, which it rarely is, the young die after a few hours. The young swift, on the other hand, is adapted to withstand the loss of a large proportion of its body weight. Where the weight curve for a young songbird shows a smooth and steady increase, the curve for a young swift increases regularly only if the weather stays clear. In England the curve for the swift is interrupted by sharp drops, each of which corresponds to a spell of bad weather. At such times the bird uses up stores of fat. It also conserves its resources for the most vital functions. A young songbird usually grows feathers at the same rate however much food it receives, so that each nestling is capable of flight on the same day. If for any reason food is somewhat scarce, the nestlings leave the nest fully equipped but underweight. Conversely the growth of feathers on the young swift in greatly retarded when food is short. As a result the length of time between the hatching of a swift and its departure from the nest varies from only five weeks when food is abundant to as much as eight weeks when it is scarce.

The young swift has another unusual adaptation. A nestling songbird must keep warm to survive. Hence before it has grown feathers it is brooded by one of its parents, while afterward it maintains its own temperature control. Since both parent swifts may have to hunt all day, their naked young are able to survive long periods without warmth. But even after young swifts have grown feathers and acquired temperature control, they can lose it again when food is scarce. They revert to a "cold-blooded" state, thus conserving their resources for the vital functions. Only two other kinds of birds are known to lose their temperature control without harm: hummingbirds during cool nights and the California poorwill during hibernation.

Eventually the young swift is ready to leave the nest. A few hours after dawn, following some preliminary hesitations, it tips gently out of the hole and flies away. The parents do not know it has gone until they return with a final, and now unnecessary, meal. From the first the fledgling is completely independent of its parents, and it never returns to the nest. Although it has never before seen the world (except downwards through the small entrance to the nest) it must immediately find all its own food. It is almost certain that it simultaneously starts on its migration to Africa.

But not all young swifts survive to leave the nest. Some die of starvation, particularly during bad summers. One of the fundamental problems that interested us was why not only swifts but also other species of birds lay eggs in a clutch of characteristic size. The swift usually lays either two or three eggs a season. Presumably it is disadvantageous for it to lay more, and in fact we were able to show that two or three eggs resulted in the most efficient family size. Our combined figures showed that only 16 per cent of the young from broods of two died (usually of starvation), whereas as many as 42 per cent from broods of three died. As a result the average number of young raised by each pair was 1.7, whether they started with two or three. It seems clear that the swift cannot normally raise more than two or three young per season and that its clutch size has been adapted by natural selection to this state of affairs. In good summers the most efficient brood size proved to be three; in bad summers it was two.

As far as we know adult swifts cannot, like their young, lose their temperature control to conserve their resources. But when the weather is very cold for a long time, they have the remarkable habit of alighting on walls in groups and clinging tightly together. In this manner they keep warm like bees in their hives during the winter. More often, however, swifts respond to adverse feeding conditions by moving elsewhere. During a heavy rain, when there are no insects in the air, the birds that are near their nesting holes come in for shelter, while the others fly away from the storm and do not return until it has passed. While we watched swift nests from the outside we were sometimes drenched by passing storms, but soon afterward we saw swifts returning with their feathers quite dry.

Sometimes their flight to avoid bad weather is an extraordinarily long one. In the middle of the breeding season on the east coast of England we have seen several hundred swifts arrive from the east, apparently having crossed at last 100 miles of sea. In Scandinavia similar flights sometimes involve thousands of birds. A Finnish worker has shown that these movements occur during the passage of cold fronts, and that the birds avoid the rain by flying against the wind. This is an effective way to get out of an area of low barometric pressure. It is supposed that such midsummer movements involve yearling birds, because swifts do not breed until they are two years old and at that time the parents cannot leave their young. This view is supported by the fact that a swift banded as a nestling at Oxford one year was recovered the following summer in the Danish province of Jutland, 550 miles to the northeast. Presumably it was on a weather movement at the time.

Although the yearling swifts do not breed, they frequent the colonies during the breeding season, selecting holes, forming pairs and even building nests. They have another habit which is perhaps the most remarkable of all those observed in the swift. Just before dark on clear, still evenings swifts collect in flocks near the colonies and gradually ascend in circles, screaming as they rise, until finally they vanish from sight. Only the yearlings do this, and they do not come back to their holes that night. Because swifts have been seen descending from great height soon after dawn, it is assumed that they spent the night in the air. It is also recorded that during the First World War an airplane pilot flew through a flock of swifts at night. This habit is unique among birds. Why swifts have it is unknown, but one wonders whether suitable roosting places are scarce in their African winter quarters, and whether there they regularly spend the night on the wing.

PART 3 THE SOCIAL INSECTS

I. THE LANGUAGE OF THE BEES
by August Krogh

The Danish physiologist August Krogh was awarded the 1920 Nobel prize in Medicine for his discovery of the capillary motor regulatory system. Krogh, who was also deeply interested in insect physiology, considered the work of Karl von Frisch, on which he writes here, to be of unrivaled importance. He wrote this article in 1948, a year before his death.

II. THE ARMY ANT
by T. C. Schneirla and Gerard Piel

While still a graduate student, T. C. Schneirla selected the ant as a promising subject for psychological study. His doctoral investigation on *Learning and Orientation in Ants* led into experiments on insect and mammalian learning as well as into a systematic study of social insects. As a test case of the "instinct" problem, he selected the many-fabled army ant. Since 1932, he has carried out ten expeditions to various parts of the American tropics devoted to the study of these creatures. Gerard Piel is publisher of SCIENTIFIC AMERICAN.

III. THE TERMITE AND THE CELL
by Martin Lüscher

This chapter reflects its author's training as an embryologist which preceded his choice of entomology as a career. Martin Lüscher teaches experimental zoology at the University of Basel, Switzerland, and is a member of the Swiss Tropical Institute. Readers who inhabit wooden houses will be interested to know that his work at the Institute is concerned with the practical as well as the purely interesting aspects of termite physiology and behavior. He was born in Basel in 1917 and got his Ph.D. at the University there in 1944. In the U. S., on a Rockefeller Foundation Fellowship, he worked with Carroll Williams, author of a later chapter in this book.

THE LANGUAGE OF THE BEES

by August Krogh

KARL VON FRISCH, the Austrian naturalist, began working with bees about forty years ago when he showed that, contrary to prevalent opinion, these insects are not entirely color-blind. From that beginning, he went on to a lifelong study of the other senses of bees and of many lower animals, especially fish. The experiments to be described here were almost all made after the last war in a small private laboratory that Von Frisch maintains at Brunnwinkl in the Austrian Alps.

Von Frisch's early experiments showed that bees must possess some means of communication, because when a rich source of food (he used concentrated sugar solution) is found by one bee, the food is soon visited by numerous other bees from the same hive. To find out how they communicated with one another, Von Frisch constructed special hives containing only one honeycomb, which could be exposed to view through a glass plate. Watching through the glass, he discovered that bees returning from a rich source of food perform special movements, which he called dancing, on the vertical surface of the honeycomb. Von Frisch early distinguished between two types of dance: the circling dance (*Rundtanz*) and the wagging dance (*Schwänzeltanz*). In the latter a bee runs a certain distance in a straight line, wagging its abdomen very swiftly from side to side, and then makes a turn. Von Frisch concluded from his early experiments that the circling dance meant nectar and the wagging dance pollen, but this turned out to be an erroneous translation as will presently appear.

In any case, the dance excites the bees. Some of them follow the dancer closely, imitating the movements, and then go out in search of the food indicated. They know what kind of food to seek from the odor of the nectar or pollen, some of which sticks to the body of the bee. By means of some ingenious experiments, Von Frisch determined that the odor of the nectar collected by bees, as well as that adhering to their bodies, is important. He designed an arrangement for feeding bees odoriferous nectar so that their body surfaces were kept from contact with it. This kind of feeding was perfectly adequate to guide the other bees. In another experiment, nectar having the odor of phlox was fed to bees as they sat on cyclamen flowers. When the bees had only a short distance to fly back to the hive, some of their fellows would go for cyclamen, but in a long flight the cyclamen odor usually was lost completely, and the bees were guided only by the phlox odor.

The vigor of the dance which guides the bees is determined by the ease with which the nectar is obtained. When the supply of nectar in a certain kind of flower begins to give out, the bees visiting it slow down or stop their dance. The result of this precisely regulated system of communication is that the bees form groups just large enough to keep up with the supply of food furnished by a given kind of flower. Von Frisch proved this by marking with a colored stain a group of bees frequenting a certain feeding place. The group was fed a sugar solution impregnated with a specific odor. When the supply of food at this place gave out, the members of the group sat idle in the hive. At intervals one of them investigated the feeding place, and if a fresh supply was provided, it would fill itself, dance on returning and rouse the group. Continued energetic dancing roused other bees sitting idle and associated them to the group.

But what was the meaning of the circling and wagging dances? Von Frisch eventually conceived the idea that the type of dance did not signify the kind of food, as he had first thought, but had something to do with the distance of the feeding place. This hypothesis led to the following crucial experiment. He trained two groups of bees from the same hive to feed at separate places. One group, marked with a blue stain, was taught to visit a feeding place only a few meters from the hive; the other, marked red, was fed at a distance of 300 meters. To the experimenter's delight, it developed that all the blue bees made circling dances; the red, wagging dances. Then, in a series of steps, Von Frisch moved the nearer feeding place farther and farther from the hive. At a distance between 50 and 100 meters away, the blue bees switched from a circling dance to wagging. Conversely, when the red group's food was brought gradually nearer to the hive, the dance changed from wagging to circling in the 50 to 100 meter range.

Thus it was clear that the dance at least told the bees whether the distance exceeded a certain value. It appeared unlikely, however, that the information conveyed was actually quite so vague, for bees often feed at distances up to two miles and presumably need more precise guidance. The wagging dance was therefore studied more closely. The rate of wagging is probably significant, but it is too rapid to follow. It was found, however, that the frequency of turns would give a fairly good indication of the distance. When the feeding place was 100 meters away, the bee made about 10 short turns in 15 seconds. To indicate a distance of 3,000 meters, it made only 3 long ones in the same time. A curve plotted from the average of performances by a number of bees shows that the number of turns varies regularly with the distance, although the correspondence is not very precise in individual cases.

How accurately do the bees respond to what is told them? Von Frisch studied this problem with several experiments, of which the following is the most conclusive. The feeding table was placed in a certain direction and at four different distances in four trials. At each trial plates containing the same odor but no food were placed in the three other directions and in each case at nearly the same distance as the food source. At short distances (about 10 meters) the bees searched almost equally in all directions. But beginning at about 25 meters they evidently had some indication of the right direction, for the plate with food was visited by much larger numbers than the plates at the other points of the compass.

How did the returning bees indicate to the other bees in the hive the direction of the feeding place? A key to the answer was given by the known fact that bees use the sun for orientation during flight. A bee caught far from the hive and liberated after a few minutes will fly straight back. But if it is kept in a dark box for a period, say an hour, it will go astray, because it continues to fly at the same angle to the sun's direction as when it was caught. Von Frisch deduced that the bee dance must signal direction in relation to the position of the sun. Obviously a horizontal direction cannot actually be shown on the vertical surface of a honeycomb, but Von Frisch discovered that the bees transpose direction and designate the top of the comb as the horizontal position of the sun. When the sun, as seen from the beehive, is just above the feeding place, the straight part of the dance is vertical with the head up. When the feeding place is in the opposite direction, the straight part again is vertical, but with the head down. And when the food is not in line with the sun, the bee shows the horizontal angle between the sun and the feeding place by pointing at the same angle from the vertical on the honeycomb.

This indication of direction changes continuously throughout the day with the changing position of the sun, which is always represented on the vertical. The dance is normally performed in complete darkness within the hive, yet the bees, roused by, following and imitating the dancer, correctly interpret the signals to an accuracy within a few degrees. It can be observed without disturbing the bees in photographic red light, which is invisible to them.

It is a very curious fact, for which no explanation has been found so far, that the position of the sun in the heavens is correctly used by the bees even when it is hidden behind an unbroken layer of clouds, and when in addition the hive is placed in surroundings totally unknown to the bees. This precaution is necessary because in territory that the bees know well they are experts in using landmarks. It appears possible that infrared rays from the sun, penetrating the clouds, may guide the bees. Experiments have shown that bees are not stimulated by heat rays as such, but the possibility cannot be excluded that the eyes of bees could be sensitive to near infrared although insensitive to visible red. This point has not so far been investigated for lack of a suitable light filter. Von Frisch has also undertaken some experiments to determine how the bees would cope with the problem of a mountain ridge or tall building which forced them to make a detour. He found that they would indicate the airline direction from the hive to the feeding place, but would give the distance that they actually had to fly.

Von Frisch tells me that he himself considered some of these results so fantastic that he had to make sure that ordinary bees which had not been experimentally trained could also do the tricks. They could, and moreover they continued to work efficiently on honeycombs removed from the hive. While studying these "wild" bees, Von Frisch became curious to see what would happen if the honeycomb was put in a horizontal position instead of the vertical. To his surprise the bees responded by pointing directly toward the feeding place, and they kept on doing this even when the honeycomb was slowly rotated like a turntable. It looked as if the bees had a magnet in them and responded like a compass needle, but experiments showed them to be not the least affected by magnetic force. This method of pointing also takes place under natural conditions, the bees often performing horizontal dances in front of the entrance to the hive.

On the other hand, experiments showed that on the underside of a horizontal surface the bees were unable to indicate any direction, and it turned out that their signals were disturbed when the horizontal surface was placed in the shade. Von Frisch therefore decided to test directly their power of indicating direction on a horizontal surface in the dark. A movable chamber was built to enclose the observer and the observation hive. By photographic red light or even by diffuse white light in a tent, the bees proved unable to indicate any direction on a horizontal surface (although they can work with precision in the dark on a vertical one). They were not restrained from dancing, and the stimulated bees, thoroughly confused, searched for food equally in all directions. The sun can be replaced in these experiments by any artificial light source of sufficient strength. But only if such a light is placed in the direction corresponding to that of the sun at the time, are the bees led toward the feeding place. Placed in any other position, the light will lead them astray.

At this point, some contradictory evidence turned up. On several occasions the bees had proved able to give correct instructions on a horizontal surface even when the sun was not directly visible. Therefore, the experiment was made of removing the north wall of the observation chamber, which allowed the bees to see only the sunless sky. In clear weather this proved sufficient to give them the correct orientation. Indeed, it was eventually found that when light from a blue sky came into the chamber through a tube 40 centimeters long and only 15 centimeters in diameter, this bare glimpse of the sky sufficed to orient the bees toward the sun's position. Light from a cloud, however, was without effect when seen through the tube, and sky light reflected by a mirror was misleading. The most probable explanation is that the bees are able to observe the direction of the polarized light from the sky and thereby infer the sun's position.

When the honeycomb is tipped to an inclination between vertical and horizontal, the bees respond by giving information that combines direct pointing with use of the vertical to indicate the sun's position. This of course results in a deviation from the true course. Analysis of earlier experiments, in which light from the sky complicated the reactions of bees on a vertical honeycomb, showed that the perturbations could all be quantitatively explained on the same basis.

I have tried to give a very condensed account of the principal results which Von Frisch has so far obtained. This series of experiments constitutes a most beautiful example of what the human mind can accomplish by tireless effort on a very high level of intelligence. But I would ask you to give some thought also to the mind of the bees. I have no doubt that some will attempt to "explain" the performance of the bees as the result of reflexes and instincts. Such attempts will certainly contribute to our understanding, but for my part I find it difficult to assume that such perfection and flexibility in behavior can be reached without some kind of mental processes—I do not venture to proclaim them as "thoughts"—going on in the small heads of the bees.

THE ARMY ANT

by T. C. Schneirla and Gerard Piel

Wherever they pass, all the rest of the animal world is thrown into a state of alarm. They stream along the ground and climb to the summit of all the lower trees searching every leaf to its apex. Where booty is plentiful, they concentrate all their forces upon it, the dense phalanx of shining and quickly moving bodies, as it spreads over the surface, looking like a flood of dark-red liquid. All soft-bodied and inactive insects fall an easy prey to them, and they tear their victims in pieces for facility in carriage. Then, gathering together again in marching order, onward they move, the margins of the phalanx spread out at times like a cloud of skirmishers from the flanks of an army.

THAT IS HOW Henry Walter Bates, a Victorian naturalist, described the characteristic field maneuvers of a tribe of army ants. His language is charged with martial metaphor, but it presents with restraint a spectacle which other eyewitnesses have compared to the predatory expeditions of Genghis Khan and Attila the Hun.

Army ants abound in the tropical rain forests of Hispanic America, Africa and Asia. They are classified taxonomically into more than 200 species and distinguished as a group chiefly by their peculiar mode of operation. Organized in colonies 100,000 to 150,000 strong, they live off their environment by systematic plunder and pillage. They are true nomads, having no fixed abode. Their nest is a seething cylindrical cluster of themselves, ant hooked to

ant, with queen and brood sequestered in a labyrinth of corridors and chambers within the ant mass. From these bivouacs they stream forth at dawn in tightly organized columns and swarms to raid the surrounding terrain. Their columns often advance as much as 35 meters an hour and may finally reach out 300 meters or more in an unbroken stream. For days at a time, they may keep their bivouacs fixed in a hollow tree or some other equally protected shelter. Then, for a restless period, they move on with every dusk. They swarm forth in a solemn, plodding procession, each ant holding to its place in line, its forward-directed antennae beating a hypnotic rhythm. At the rear come throngs of larvae-carriers and, at the very last, the big, wingless queen, buried under a melee of frenzied workers. Late at night they hang their new bivouac under a low branch or pine.

The army ant, observers are agreed, presents the most complex instance of organized mass behavior occurring regularly outside the homesite in any insect or, for that matter, in any subhuman animal. As such, it offers the student of animal psychology a subject rich in interest for itself. But it also provides an opportunity for original attack on some basic problems of psychology in general. The study here reported, covering the behavior of two of the Eciton species of army ants, was conducted by Schneirla over a twenty-year period with extended field trips to the Biological Reservation on Barro Colorado Island in the Panama Canal Zone and to other ant haunts in Central America. In undertaking it, he had certain questions in mind. The central question, of course, was how such an essentially primitive creature as the ant manages such a highly organized and complex social existence. This bears on the more general consideration of organized group behavior as an adaptive device in natural selection. There was, finally, the neglected question of the nature of social organization. This is primarily a psychological problem because it concerns the contribution of individual behavior and relationships between individuals to the pattern of the group as a whole. It was expected that reliable data on these questions in the instance of the army ant might throw light on similar questions about human societies.

The ant commends itself to study by man. Measured by the dispassionate standard of survival, it stands as one of the most successful of nature's inventions. It is the most numerous of all land animals both in number of individuals and number of species (more than 3,500 at present count). It has occupied the whole surface of the globe between the margins of eternal frost.

The oldest of living families, the ant dates back more than 65 million years to the early Jurassic period. More significant, the societies of ants probably evolved to their present state of perfection no less than 50 million years ago. Man, by contrast, is a dubious experiment in evolution that has barely got under way.

Lord Avebury, a British myrmecologist, marveled at "the habits of ants, their large communities and elaborate habitations, their roadways, possession of domestic animals and even, in some cases, of slaves!" He might have added that ants also cultivate agricultural crops and carry parasols. It is the social institutions of ants, however, that engender the greatest astonishment. The sight of an army ant bivouac put the British naturalist Thomas Belt in mind of Sir Thomas More's *Utopia.* The Swiss naturalist Auguste Forel urged the League of Nations to adopt the ant polity as the model for the world community.

The marvels of ant life have led some thinkers into giddy speculation on the nature of ant intelligence. Few have put themselves so quaintly on record as Lord Avebury, who declared: "The mental powers of ants differ from those of men not so much in kind as in degree." He ranked them ahead of the anthropoid apes. Maeterlinck was more cautious: "After all, we have not been present at the deliberations of the workers and we know hardly anything of what happens in the depths of the formicary." Others have categorically explained ant behavior as if the creatures could reason, exchange information, take purposeful action and feel tender emotion.

Obviously anthropomorphism can explain little about ants, and it has largely disappeared from the current serious literature about ant behavior. Its place has been taken, however, by errors of a more sophisticated sort. One such is the concept of the "superorganism." This derives from a notion entertained by Plato and Aquinas that a social organization exhibits the attributes of a superior type of individual. Extended by certain modern biologists, the concept assumes that the biological organism, a society of cells, is the model for social organizations, whether ant or human. Plausible analogies are drawn between organisms and societies: division of function, internal communication, rhythmic periodicity of life processes and the common cycle of birth, growth, senescence and death. Pursuit of these analogies, according to the protagonists of the superorganism, will disclose that the same forces of natural selection have shaped the evolution of both organism and superorganism, and that the same fundamental laws govern their present existence.

This is a thoroughly attractive idea, but it possesses a weakness common to all Platonistic thinking. It erects a vague concept, "organism" or "organization," as an ultimate reality which defies explanation. The danger inherent in this arbitrary procedure is the bias it encourages in the investigator's approach to his problem. The social scientist must impose on his work the same rules of repetition, systematic variation and control that prevail in the experimental sciences. Wherever possible he should subject his observations to experimental tests in the field and laboratory. In the area we are discussing this kind of work may at times seem more like a study of ants than an investigation of problems. But it yields dependable data.

The individual ant is not equipped for mammalian types of learning. By comparison with the sensitive perceptions of a human being, it is deaf and blind. Its hearing consists primarily in the perception of vibrations physically transmitted to it through the ground. In most species, its vision is limited to the discrimination of light and shadow. These deficiencies are partially compensated by the chemotactual perceptions of the ant, centered in its flitting antennae. Chiefly by means of its antennae, the army ant tells friend from foe, locates its booty, and, thanks to its habit of blazing its trail with organic products such as droplets from its anal gland, finds its way home to the nest. In any case, the ant has little need of learning when it crawls out of the cocoon. By far the greater part of its behavior pattern is already written in its genes.

How the essentially uncomplicated repertory of the individual ant contrives, when ants act in concert, to yield the exceedingly complex behavior of the tribe is one of the most intricate paradoxes in nature. This riddle has been fruitfully explored during the past generation under the guidance of the concept of "trophallaxis," originated by the late William Morton Wheeler of Harvard University, who ranks as the greatest of U. S. myrmecologists. Trophallaxis (from the Greek *trophe,* meaning food, and *allaxis,* exchange) is based upon the familiar observation that ants live in biological thrall to their nest-mates. Their powerful mutual attraction can be seen in the constant turning of one ant toward another, the endless antennal caresses, the licking and nuzzling. In these exchanges they can be seen trading intimate substances—regurgitated food and glandular secretions. Most ants are dependent for their lives upon this biosocial intercourse with their fellows. There is strong evidence that an interchange of co-enzymes among larvae, workers and queen is necessary to the survival of all three. Army ant queens unfailingly sicken and die after a few days of isolation.

The well-established concept of trophallaxis naturally suggests that clues to the complex behavior of the ant armies should be sought in the relationships among individuals within the tribe.

Most investigators have looked elsewhere, with invariably mistaken results. In attempting to explain, for example, why an ant army alternates between periods of fixed bivouac and nomadic wandering, a half-dozen reputable scientists have jumped to the simplest and most disarmingly logical conclusion: food supply. The ants, they declared, stay in one place until they exhaust the local larder and then move on to new hunting grounds. Schneirla has shown, however, that the true explanation is quite different.

The migratory habits of the ant armies follow a rhythmically punctual cycle. The *Eciton hamatum* species, for example, wanders nomadically for a period of 17 days, then spends 19 or 20 days in fixed bivouac. This cycle coincides precisely with the reproductive cycle of the tribe. The army goes into bivouac when the larvae, hatched from the last clutch of eggs, spin their cocoons and, now quiescent, approach the pupal stage. At the end of the first week in permanent camp, the queen, whose abdomen has swollen to more than five times its normal volume, begins a stupendous five- to seven-day labor and delivers the 20,000 to 30,000 eggs of the next generation. The daily foraging raids, which meanwhile have dwindled to a minimum, pick up again as the eggs hatch into a great mass of larvae. Then, on about the 20th day, the cocoons yield a new complement of callow workers, and the army sets off once more on its evening marches. The rise and fall of this rhythm is shown in the accompanying sketch.

In determining this pattern of events Schneirla logged a dozen ant armies through one or more complete cycles, and upwards of 100 through partial cycles. Observations were set down in shorthand in the field. In the course of the last field trip, from February to July 1953, broods of more than 80 colonies were sampled, most of them repeatedly at intervals of a few days.

A sentimentalist presented with this new picture of the army ant's domestic habits will perhaps decide that the ants stay in fixed bivouac to protect the queen and her helpless young through the time when they are most vulnerable. Doubtless this is the adaptive significance of the process. But the motivation which carries 100,000 to 150,000 individual ants through this precisely timed cycle of group behavior is not familial love and duty but the trophallactic relationship among the members of the tribe. A cocooned and slumberous pupa, for example, exerts a quieting influence upon the worker that clutches it in its mandible—somewhat as a thumb in the mouth pacifies an infant. But as it approaches maturity and quickens within its cocoon, the pupa produces precisely the reverse effect. Its stirring and twitching excite the workers to pick up the cocoon and snatch it from one another. As an incidental result, this manhandling effects the delivery of the cocoon's occupant.

The stimulus of the emerging brood is evident in a rising crescendo of excitement that seizes the whole community. Raiding operations increase in tempo as the hyperactive, newly delivered workers swarm out into the marching columns. After a day or two, the colony stages an exceptionally vigorous raid which ends in a

Life cycle of army ant tribe is governed by closely interlocked cycles of behavior (above) and reproduction (below). Rhythm is established in large part by punctuality of queen's five-week cycle of ovulation. She goes into labor at end of first week of the statary phase of the behavior cycle and lays 20,000 to 30,000 eggs in next few days. At this time, tribe is in fixed bivouac, and workers are conducting minimal daily foraging raids. Statary phase continues for another 10 days, long enough for eggs to develop into larvae and for preceding generation of larvae to come through the pupal stage and yield a crop of callow workers. Chemical and physical stimuli of wriggling larvae and hyperactive callows now help to energize the nomadic phase of the behavior cycle, in which vigorous raiding induces daily change of bivouac. During this 17-day period, callows merge into the ranks of mature workers, the larvae attain their growth and start spinning cocoons, and the queen's gaster begins to swell with eggs. Raiding diminishes, and the tribe settles again in a fixed bivouac. This synchronism of behavior and reproductive cycles, providing maximum security at the successive biological crises of reproduction, plays an obviously critical role in the survival of the species.

17 day 19-20

STATARY NOMADIC STATARY NOMADIC STATARY

night march. The bivouac site is left littered with empty cocoons. Later in the nomadic phase, as the stimulus of the callow workers wanes, the larvae of the next generation become the source of colony "drive." Fat and squirming, as big as an average worker, they establish an active trophallactic relationship with the rest of the tribe. Workers constantly stroke them with their antennae, lick them with their mouth parts and carry them bodily from place to place. Since the larvae at this stage are usually well distributed throughout the corridors and the chambers of the overnight bivouac, their stimulus reaches directly a large number of the workers. This is reflected in the sustained vigor of the daily raids, which continue until the larvae spin their cocoons.

These observations are supported by a variety of experimental findings in the field and laboratory. The role of the callow workers in initiating the movement to break bivouac was confirmed by depriving a number of colonies of their callow broods. Invariably, the raiding operations of the colony failed to recover from the lethargic state that is characteristic of the statary phases. Some tribes even extended their stay in fixed bivouac until the larvae grew large and active enough to excite the necessary pitch of activity. To test the role of the larval brood, captured tribes were divided into part-colonies of comparable size. The group with larvae showed much greater activity than those that had no larvae or that had cocoons in the early pupal state.

The interrelationships among members of the colony thus provide a complete explanation for the behavior cycle of the army ant. It should be observed, in conclusion, that the whole complex process is carried out by individuals which do not themselves originate the basic motivations of their behavior.

Long before the intricacies of its domestic existence were suspected, the army ant's reputation as a social animal was firmly established by its martial conduct in external affairs. It does not require an overactive imagination to perceive the classic doctrines

of offensive warfare in the action of an ant army in the field. The swarm carries through the maneuvers of wheeling, flanking and envelopment with a ruthless precision. But to find its motivations and explain its mechanics, one must consult the ant, not von Clausewitz.

Army ant raids fall into one of two major patterns. They are organized either in dense swarms which form at the head of the column or in a delicate tracery of capillary columns branching out at the forward end of the main raiding column. Both types of raiding are found in subgenera of each of the common species of Central American army ant. Two species of Eciton (*Eciton*) were selected for this study because they lead their life almost altogether on or above the forest floor and are thus accessible to continuous observation. Whether the army ants raid in swarm or column, however, the essential mechanics of their behavior are substantially the same.

The bivouac awakes in the early dawn. The stir of activity begins when the light (as measured by photometer) reaches .05 foot candles, and it mounts steadily as the light increases. In strands and clusters, the workers tumble out of the bivouac into a churning throng on the ground. A crowding pressure builds up within this throng until, channeled by the path of least resistance, a raiding column suddenly bursts forth. The ants in the column are oriented rigidly along the line of travel blazed by the chemical trail of the leaders. The minims and medium-sized workers move in tight files in the center. The "workers major," displaced by the unstable footing afforded by the backs of their smaller fellows, travel along each side. This arrangement no doubt lends suggestive support to the major's legendary role of command. It has an adaptive significance in that it places the biggest and most formidable of the workers on the flanks. Unless disturbed, however, the majors hug the column as slavishly as the rest. The critical role of the tribal chemical in creating this drill sergeant's picture of order may be demonstrated by a simple field experiment. Removal of the chemically saturated litter from the trail brings the column to an abrupt halt. A traffic jam of ants piles up on the bivouac side of the break and is not relieved until enough ants have been pushed forward to re-establish the chemical trail.

Appearances are less ordered at the front of the column, where the "scouts" and "skirmishers" are most frequently observed. The timid individual behavior of the forward ants scarcely justifies such titles. The Eciton is a far from enterprising forager. It never ventures more than a few inches into the chemically-free area ahead. Even this modest pioneering is stimulated principally by physical impact from the rear. At the end of its brief sally, the Eciton rebounds quickly into the column. It is here that the critical difference between column and swarm raiding arises. The column-raiding ants are somewhat freer in their pioneering behavior and so open new pathways more readily. In the swarm raiders the comparatively reluctant progress of the forward elements creates a counterpressure against the progress of the column. This forces the head of the column into a broad elliptical swarm which arrays itself at right angles to the line of march. With ants pouring in from behind, the swarm grows steadily in size as it moves forward, often achieving a width of more than 15 meters.

The path of an ant army, whether in swarms or columns, shows no evidence of leadership. On the contrary, each individual makes substantially the same contribution to the group behavior pattern. The army's course is directed by such wholly chance factors as the stimulus of booty and the character of the terrain. On close inspection, therefore, it appears that the field operations of ant armies approximate the principles of hydraulics even more closely than those of military tactics. This impression is confirmed by analysis of the flanking maneuver as executed by the swarm raiders. A shimmering pattern of whirls, eddies and momentarily milling vortices of ants, the swarm advances with a peculiar rocking motion. First one and then the other end of the elliptical swarm surges forward. This action results in the outflanking of quarry, which is swiftly engulfed in the overriding horde of ants. It arises primarily, however, from an interplay of forces within the swarm. One of these forces is generated by the inrush of ants from the rear. Opposed by the hesitant progress of the swarm, the new arrivals are deflected laterally to the wing which offers least resistance. This wing moves forward in a wheeling motion until pressure from the slow advance of its frontal margins counterbalances the pressure from the rear. Pressure on the opposite wing has meanwhile been relieved by drainage of the ants into the flanking action. The cycle is therewith reversed, and a new flanking action gets under way from the other end. External factors, too, play a role in this cycle. The stimulus of booty will accelerate the advance of a flank. The capture of booty will halt it and bring ants stampeding in for a large-scale mopping-up party. But raiding activity as such is only incidental to the process. Its essential character is determined by the stereotyped behavior of the individual ant with its limited repertory of responses to external stimuli.

The profoundly simple nature of the beast is betrayed by an ironic catastrophe which occasionally overtakes a troop of army ants. It can happen only under certain very special conditions. But when these are present, army ants are literally fated to organize themselves in a circular column and march themselves to death. Post-mortem evidence of this phenomenon has been found in nature; it may be arranged at will in the laboratory. Schneirla has had the good fortune to observe one such spectacle in nature almost from its inception to the bitter end.

The ants, numbering about 1,000, were discovered at 7:30 A.M. on a broad concrete sidewalk on the grounds of the Barro Colorado laboratories. They had apparently been caught by a cloudburst which washed away all traces of their colony trail. When first observed, most of the ants were gathered in a central cluster, with only a company or two plodding, counterclockwise, in a circle around the periphery. By noon all of the ants had joined the mill, which had now attained the diameter of a phonograph record and was rotating somewhat eccentrically at fair speed. By 10:00 P.M. the mill had divided into two smaller counterclockwise spinning discs. At dawn the next day the scene of action was strewn with dead and dying Ecitons. A scant three dozen survivors were still trekking in a ragged circle. By 7:30, 24 hours after the mill was first observed, the various small myrmicine and dolichoderine ants of the neighborhood were busy carting away the corpses.

This peculiarly Eciton calamity may be described as tragic in the classic meaning of the Greek drama. It arises, like Nemesis, out of the very aspects of the ant's nature which most plainly characterize its otherwise successful behavior. The general mechanics of the mill are fairly obvious. The circular track represents the vector of the individual ant's centrifugal impulse to resume the march and the centripetal force of trophallaxis which binds it to its group. Where no obstructions disturb the geometry of these forces, the organization of a suicide mill is almost inevitable. Fortunately for the army ant, the jungle terrain, with its random layout of roots and vines, leaves and stones, disarrays the symmetry of forces and liberates the ant from its propensity to destroy itself.

The army ant suicide mill provides an excellent occasion for considering the comparative nature of social behavior and organization at the various levels from ants to men. Other animals occasionally give themselves over to analogous types of mass action. Circular mills are common among schools of herring. Stampeding cattle, sheep jumping fences blindly in column and other instances of pell-mell surging by a horde of animals are familiar phenomena. Experience tells us that men, too, can act as a mob. These analogies are the stock-in-trade of the "herd instinct" schools of sociology and politics.

We are required, however, to look beyond the analogy and study the relationship of the pattern to other factors of individual and group behavior in the same species. In the case of the army ant, the circular column really typifies the animal. Among mammals, such simplified mass behavior occupies a clearly subordinate role. Their group activity patterns are chiefly characterized by great plasticity and capacity to adjust to new stituations. This observation applies with special force to the social potentialities of man. When human societies begin to march in circular columns, the cause is to be found in the strait-jacket influence of the man-made social institutions which foster such behavior.

As for "specialization of functions," that is determined in insect societies by specialization in the biological makeup of individuals. Mankind, in contrast, is biologically uniform and homogeneous. Class and caste distinctions among men are drawn on a psychological basis. They break down constantly before the energies and talents of particular individuals.

Finally, the concept of "organization" itself, as it is used by the superorganism theorists, obscures a critical distinction between the societies of ants and men. The social organizations of insects are fixed and transmitted by heredity. But members of each generation of men may, by exercise of the cerebral cortex, increase, change and even displace given aspects of their social heritage. This is a distinction which has high ethical value for men when they are moved to examine the conditions of their existence.

THE TERMITE AND THE CELL

by Martin Lüscher

TERMITES, closely related to the roaches, are relatively primitive insects which have nevertheless developed extremely elaborate social habits. There are no solitary termites. Of about 2,000 known species, all have at least three structurally different forms, which live together as castes with different functions in the colony. Some have as many as six or seven easily distinguishable castes.

Each caste generally possesses its own special instincts. The king and queen, which develop from winged forms that lose their wings after the nuptial flight, start the colony. They are extremely well adapted to their single occupation of reproduction: some tropical queens lay as many as 20,000 eggs a day. When they die, nymphs in the colony develop into a special caste to take over their procreative function. These nymphs grow reproductive organs, molt and become fertile. They are called supplementary reproductives.

All other castes in the colony are sterile, though they contain both sexes. There are soldier castes equipped with enormous jaws to defend the colony against predators. Many species also have worker castes, which build the nests and runways, collect food to feed the colony, and take care of the eggs. Termite species of the temperate regions usually have no true worker caste; their growing nymphs do the work.

The caste arrangement among the termites has attracted investigators for a long time. Early authorities thought that the differences among the castes were hereditary, but it is now known that they develop according to the needs of the colony, just as the embryonic cells of a single animal differentiate into blood cells, bone cells, muscle cells and so on. Thus a colony of termites is a kind of superorganism in which we can study differentiation in a nice, convenient way.

It was the late S. F. Light and his colleagues at the University of California who demonstrated that the caste of a termite is not fixed by its genes. They discovered that any nymph in a colony of termites could develop into either a soldier or a king or queen of the supplementary type, depending on what the situation demanded. For example, in the species of damp-wood termites they studied, a new colony always has one soldier, and only one, in the first brood. When they removed the soldier, another always developed, from a nymph which would not normally have become a soldier. This occurred up to as many as six times; each time a soldier developed to replace the one removed. Likewise the elimination of reproductive termites caused replacements to develop.

Light's group concluded that the soldier and reproductive termites already present in a colony inhibited the development of additional ones, and that they exercised this inhibition by means of some kind of "social hormone." To test this theory the experimenters fed extracts from reproductive termites to developing nymphs. There was a slight inhibition in the production of new kings and queens and a delay in egg-laying, but the effect was not sufficiently clearcut to prove the social hormone theory. Recent experiments, however, have given the theory more definite support.

If a termite colony is considered as a superorganism, then caste differentiation may be looked upon as an embryological problem. The differentiation of cells in an embryo is always initiated at a certain critical stage in their development; in other words, a given group of cells cannot change until it is ready. One may assume that a nymph in a termite colony similarly can be induced to differentiate only at a critical stage of readiness.

We have studied the critical period in the European dry-wood termite. We marked the nymphs individually with colored spots and kept them under observation daily for two years in flat nests. They went through several molts. As individuals molted they were measured and marked again, since they lost the spots with the castoff skin. From time to time the king and queen were removed so that new reproductive termites would develop from the nymphs.

This investigation showed that there is a certain critical period during the molting interval when a nymph has the capacity to differentiate into a special adult caste. But whether it will do so depends on the makeup of the colony's population. Most of the nymphs never differentiate, though they may go on molting at regular intervals. These arrested nymphs function as workers in this species, which has no true worker caste. We call them "pseudo-workers." A pseudo-worker may develop wing pads and become a winged adult.

The pseudo-workers are the undifferentiated elements of a colony, like the undifferentiated cells of an organism. What makes them convenient for study of differentiation is that they can be followed individually, unlike the cells in an organism.

It is easy to produce new adults of the reproductive caste experimentally. All one has to do is to remove the king or queen or both from the colony. Within 10 to 20 days several supplementary reproductive adults of both sexes appear. But the colony will tolerate only one king and one queen; it promptly kills and eats the excess.

So long as the reproductive pair is present, no others are produced. Yet if the pair is removed for only 24 hours, new candidates at once begin to develop as their replacements. In that 24-hour period the differentiation of the candidate nymphs is irreversily determined. Even though the original king and queen are returned to the colony, the nymphs that have started to differentiate will go on developing and become reproductive adults in 8 to 14 days.

The capacity of a given nymph to change into a reproductive adult depends on the stage of its molting cycle. Any nymph that has just molted when the king and queen are taken away is certain to change. This capacity decreases exponentially with time after the molt: 19 days after the molt it has dropped to 50 per cent (i.e., only half of the nymphs at this stage will change), and 38 days after the molt it is only 25 per cent. The curve showing the decline in the capacity to change resembles a radioactive decay curve—the half-life period in this case being 19 days (at a temperature of 80 degrees Fahrenheit). That is, after 19 days half of the originally capable termites have lost their competence to change. As in the disintegration of radioactive atoms, we cannot predict just which individuals will lose the capacity in 19 days; all we can say is that each has a 50 per cent chance of losing it by that time.

From the fact that the loss of competence is an exponential function we may conclude that it is due in each individual to a single biochemical event, possibly the disintegration or synthesis of a specific molecule.

All this bears a striking resemblance to an embryo cell's loss of competence to change. The University of Rochester embryologist Johannes Holtfreter has made a series of transplantations of ectoderm (outer) tissue from a young amphibian embryo into the site where nerve tissue develops in another embryo. He found that the tissue he took from the donor gradually lost its competence to change into nerve tissue as he kept it in artificial culture longer and longer before implanting it. For the tissue as a whole the decline in ability to differentiate was not exponential, but for the individual cells in the tissue it very likely is, as a single cell must change or not change: there are no gradations in between. The changes in the transplanted tissue ranged from complete alteration to a spinal cord to development of only a few neural cells.

We must of course be cautious about applying the conclusions about the termite "superorganism" to an actual organism, but it seems reasonable to assume, as a working hypothesis, that the loss of ability to differentiate in cells, as in individual insects in a termite colony, is effected by a single event, possibly a change in a single molecule in each cell.

In a termite colony, as we have seen, differentiation depends on two things: (1) the nymph's competence to change, and (2) inhibition, or lack of inhibition, by the colony. How is this inhibition exerted: by some active substance, a social hormone as Light suggested, or merely by a scent or other sensory warning given off by the king and queen?

To test these possibilities we observed two colonies of termites separated by a fine metal screen through which the colonies could maintain contact by rubbing antennae. One colony had a king and queen, the other was orphaned. The termites showed a strong tendency to touch antennae through the screen. Now the experiment had a curiously mixed result. The contact through the screen did not prevent the groups from behaving, in one sense, like two separate colonies: the orphaned colony always proceeded to produce its own king and queen. But in many instances it promptly killed them, as if it perceived the king and queen on the other side of the screen and considered its own as surplus. This confusion progressed so far that the colony went on producing and killing kings and queens until it had almost annihilated itself.

When the colonies were separated by a screen which prevented any contact, the orphaned colony produced and supported its own king and queen in the normal way. On the whole the experiment upheld the idea that an active principle transmitted by contact, that is, a social hormone, is responsible for the suppression of differentiation.

It seems likely that production of the soldier caste also is regulated by an inhibitory substance. But Frances Weesner of the University of California has recently discovered that in at least one species of termite the production of soldiers is controlled by a promoting factor as well as an inhibitory one.

The upshot of all this work on termites is that the balance of castes in a termite society seems to be maintained by means of certain special hormones, produced by the differentiated adults and acting upon the undifferentiated nymphs. A similar theory would explain many facts in cell differentiation. In an organism the various kinds of differentiated cells are always kept in constant proportions. By analogy with the termite colony, we might assume that each type of cell produces a specific hormone which inhibits the production of an excessive number of cells of the same type. Some evidence for this was recently gained by S. Meryl Rose of the University of Illinois, who showed that in the presence of an amphibian animal's adult tissues the differentiation of an embryo's cells into the same tissues is inhibited.

There is another striking parallel between a termite society and an embryonic organism. Among the termites winged adults develop only in colonies with a population of at least 100. When nymphs with incipient wings are transferred from such a large colony to a small one before a critical stage of their molting cycle, they lose their wing pads at the next molt. Similarly, at one stage in the development of an embryo, differentiation occurs only if the embroyo contains a certain minimum number of undifferentiated cells. The same is true in some tissue cultures: differentiation can take place only when the culture has grown to a certain size.

The study of differentiation in termite societies has discovered so many analogies to cell differentiation that it is reasonable to expect more. The superorganism idea promises to be immensely helpful, for we can isolate and experiment on individual termites as we cannot on single cells in an embryo. We must always keep in mind, however, that an analogy can do no more than suggest a working hypothesis, which is not to be taken too seriously until it is experimentally confirmed.

PART 4 ORIGIN OF SPECIES

I. DARWIN'S FINCHES
by David Lack

In 1938, at the instigation of Julian Huxley, David Lack made the expedition to the Galapagos Islands to study the finches about which he writes here. Lack trapped thirty live birds intending to take them home to the London Zoo, of which Huxley is Keeper. But they proved to be such poor travelers that he had to leave them in California, where some of them nested successfully. His book on the subject of these birds won the Brewster Gold Medal of the American Ornithologists Union. He is a Fellow of the Royal Society.

II. THE END OF THE MOAS
by Edward S. Deevey, Jr.

Edward S. Deevey's early interest in nature and the out-of-doors around Albany, New York, won him forty-one Boy Scout merit badges and the Boy Scout Nature Prize in 1928. He took his undergraduate and graduate degrees at Yale University, specializing in limnology, the study of lakes. During the war he was at Woods Hole Oceanographic Institute where he worked on marine fouling for the Navy. Returning to Yale, he has occupied himself primarily with the ecology of the Pleistocene epoch, with excursions into modern ecology. Deevey is professor of biology and director of the Geochronological Laboratory, which was organized around his work in radiocarbon dating.

DARWIN'S FINCHES

by David Lack

On the Galapagos Islands in the Pacific Charles Darwin in 1835 saw a group of small, drab, finchlike birds which were to change the course of human history, for they provided a powerful stimulus to his speculations on the origin of species—speculations that led to the theory of evolution by natural selection. In the study of evolution the animals of remote islands have played a role out of all proportion to their small numbers. Life on such an island approaches the conditions of an experiment in which we can see the results of thousands of years of evolutionary development without outside intervention. The Galapagos finches are an admirable case study.

These volcanic islands lie on the Equator in the Pacific Ocean some 600 miles west of South America and 3,000 miles east of Polynesia. It is now generally agreed that they were pushed up out of the sea by volcanoes more than one million years ago and have never been connected with the mainland. Whatever land animals they harbor must have come over the sea, and very few species have established themselves there: just two kinds of mammals, five reptiles, six songbirds and five other land birds.

Some of these animals are indistinguishable from the same species on the mainland; some are slightly different; a few, such as the giant land-tortoises and the mockingbirds, are very different. The latter presumably reached the Galapagos a long time ago. In addition, there are variations from island to island among the local species themselves, indicating that the colonists diverged into variant forms after their arrival. Darwin's finches go further than this: not only do they vary from island to island but up to ten different species of them can be found on a single island.

The birds themselves are less dramatic than their story. They are dull in color, unmusical in song and, with one exception, undistinguished in habits. This dullness is in no way mitigated by their dreary surroundings. Darwin in his diary succinctly described the islands: "The country was compared to what we might imagine the cultivated parts of the Infernal regions to be." This diary, it is interesting to note, makes no mention of the finches, and the birds received only a brief mention in the first edition of his book on the voyage of the *Beagle.* Specimens which Darwin brought home, however, were recognized by the English systematist and bird artist, John Gould, as an entirely new group of birds. By the time the book reached its second edition, the ferment had begun to work, and Darwin added that "one might really fancy that from an original paucity of birds in this archipelago, one species had been taken and modified for different ends." Thus obscurely, as an afterthought in a travel book, man received a first intimation that he might once have been an ape.

There are thirteen species of Darwin's finches in the Galapagos, plus one on Cocos Island to the northwest. A self-contained group with no obvious relations elsewhere, these finches are usually placed in a subfamily of birds named the *Geospizinae.* How did this remarkable group evolve? I am convinced, from my observations in the islands in 1938-39 and from subsequent studies of museum specimens, that the group evolved in much the same way as other birds. Consequently the relatively simple story of their evolution can throw valuable light on the way in which birds, and other animals, have evolved in general. Darwin's finches form a little world of their own, but a world which differs from the one we know only in being younger, so that here, as Darwin wrote, we are brought nearer than usual "to that great fact—that mystery of mysteries—the first appearance of new beings on this earth."

The fourteen species of Darwin's finches fall into four main genera. First, there are the ground-finches, embracing six species, nearly all of which feed on seeds on the ground and live in the arid coastal regions. Secondly, there are the tree-finches, likewise including six species, nearly all of which feed on insects in trees and live in the moist forests. Thirdly, there is the warbler-like finch (only one species) which feeds on small insects in bushes in both arid and humid regions. Finally, there is the isolated Cocos Island species which lives on insects in a tropical forest.

Among the ground-finches, four species live together on most of the islands: three of them eat seeds and differ from each other mainly in the size of their beaks, adapted to different sizes of seeds; the fourth species feeds largely on prickly pear and has a much longer and more pointed beak. The two remaining species of ground-finches, one large and one small, live chiefly on the outlying islands, where some supplement their seed diet with cactus, their beaks being appropriately modified.

Of the tree-finches, one species is vegetarian with a parrot-like beak seemingly fitted to its diet of buds and fruits. The next three species are closely alike, differing primarily in body size and in the size of their beaks, presumably scaled to the size of the insects they take. A fifth species eats insects in mangrove swamps. The sixth species of tree-finch is one of the most remarkable birds in the world. Like a woodpecker, it climbs tree trunks in search of insects, which it excavates from the bark with its chisel-shaped beak. While its beak approaches a woodpecker's in shape it has not evolved the long tongue with which a woodpecker probes insects from crannies. Instead, this tree-finch solves the problem in another way: it carries about a cactus spine or small twig which it pokes into cracks, dropping the stick to seize any insect that emerges. This astonishing practice is one of the few recorded cases of the use of tools by any animal other than man or the apes.

The warbler-like finch is in its own way as remarkable as the Galapagos attempt at a woodpecker. It has no such wonderful habit, but in its appearance and character it has evolved much closer to a warbler than the other finch has to a woodpecker. Thus its beak is thin and pointed like that of a warbler; its feeding methods and actions are similar, and it even has the warbler-like habit of flicking its wings partly open as it hunts for food. For nearly a century it was classified as a warbler, but its internal anatomy, the color of its eggs, the shape of its nest and other characteristics clearly place it among the finches.

The close resemblance among Darwin's finches in plumage, calls, nests, eggs and display suggests that they have not yet had time to diverge far from one another. The only big difference is in their beaks, adapted to their different diets. It is reasonably certain that all the Galapagos finches evolved from one original colonizing form. What is unusual about them is the existence of several distinct species on the same island. In this we may have an indirect clue to how separate species establish themselves.

Let us consider first how new forms of an animal may originate from a common ancestor. When a member of the original species moves into a new environment, it is likely to evolve new features adapted to the new local conditions. Such geographical variations among animals are commonly found; in the Galapagos, for instance, the land birds other than finches vary from island to island, with only one form on each island. These forms are not distinct species but subspecies, or geographical races. Their differences, however, are hereditary and not trivial or accidental. There are several examples of such geographical variation among Darwin's finches. Three common species of the ground-finch, for instance, are found on most of the islands; they are large, medium and small, feeding on large, medium and small seeds respectively. Now on two southern islands the large species is missing, and here the medium species has a rather larger beak than elsewhere, presumably an adaptation to the large seeds available to it in the absence of the large species. Again, on another islet the small ground-finch is absent, and the medium species fills the gap by being rather smaller than elsewhere. On still other islets the medium species is missing and the small species is rather larger than elsewhere.

It seems clear that the beak differences among the subspecies of Darwin's finches are adaptive. Further, some of these differences are as great as those distinguishing true species.

What is likely to happen if a subspecies evolved in isolation on one island later spreads to an island occupied by another race of the same species? If the two populations have not been isolated for long and differ in only minor ways, they may interbreed freely and so merge with each other. But evidence from the study of insects suggests that if two populations have been isolated for a long time, so many hereditary differences will have accumulated that their genes will not combine well. Any hybrid offspring will not survive as well as the parent types. Hence natural selection will tend to intensify the gap between the two forms, and they will continue to evolve into two distinct species.

Darwin's finches provide circumstantial evidence for the origin of a new species by means of geographical isolation. Consider three different forms of the large insectivorous tree-finch. On the most southerly Galapagos island is a small dark form with a comparatively small beak. On another island to the northwest is a rather larger and less barred form. On the central islands is a yet larger and paler type with a larger, more parrot-like beak. Evidently these three forms had a common ancestor and evolved their differences in geographical isolation. The differences among them do not seem great enough to set them apart as separate species, and they would be classed as subspecies but for one curious circumstance: on the southernmost island the two extremes—the small dark form and the largest pale form—live side by side without merging. Clearly these must be truly separate species. It seems likely that the large pale form spread from the central islands to the southern island in comparatively recent times, after both it and the small dark form had evolved into distinct species.

If differentiated forms are to persist alongside each other as separate species, two conditions must be met. First, they must avoid interbreeding. In birds this is usually taken care of by differences in appearance (generally in the color pattern) and in the song. It is no accident that bird-watchers find male birds so easy to recognize: correct identification is even more important for the female bird! Darwin's finches recognize each other chiefly by the beak. We have often seen a bird start to chase another from behind and quickly lose interest when a front view shows that the beak is that of a species other than its own.

The second requirement for the existence of two species together is that they must not compete for the same food. If they tend to eat similar food, the one that is better adapted to obtain that food will usually eliminate the other. In those cases where two closely related species live side by side, investigation shows that they have in fact evolved differences in diet. Thus the beak differences among the various Galapagos finches are not just an insular curiosity but are adapted to differences in diet and are an essential factor in their persistence together. It used to be supposed that related species of birds overlapped considerably in their feeding habits. A walk through a wood in summer may suggest that many of the birds have similar habits. But having established the principle of food differentiation in Darwin's finches, I studied many other examples of closely related species and found that most, if not all, differ from one another in the places where they feed, in their feeding methods or in the size of the food items they can take. The appearance of overlap was due simply to inadequate knowledge.

Now the key to differentiation is geographical isolation. Probably one form can establish itself alongside another only after the two have already evolved some differences in separate places. Evolutionists used to believe that new species evolved by becoming adapted to different habitats in the same area. But there is no positive evidence for that once popular theory, and it is now thought that geographical isolation is the only method by which new species originate, at least among birds. One of Darwin's species of finches provides an interesting illustration of this. The species on Cocos Island is so different from the rest that it must have been isolated there for a long time. Yet despite this long isolation, along with a great variety of foods and habitats and a scarcity of other bird competitors, the Cocos finch has remained a single species. This is because Cocos is an isolated island, and so does not provide the proper opportunities for differentiation. In the Galapagos, differentiation was possible because the original species could scatter and establish separate homes on the various islands of the archipelago. It is significant that the only other group of birds which has evolved in a similar way, the sicklebills of Hawaii, are likewise found in an archipelago.

Why is it that this type of evolution has been found only in the Galapagos and Hawaii? There are other archipelagoes in the world, and geographical isolation is also possible on the continents. The ancestor of Darwin's finches, for instance, must formerly have lived on the American mainland, but it has not there given rise to a group of species similar to those in the Galapagos. The answer is, probably, that on the mainland the available niches in the environment were already occupied by efficient species of other birds. Consider the woodpecker-like finch on the Galapagos, for example. It would be almost impossible for this type to evolve in a land which already possessed true woodpeckers, as the latter would compete with it and eliminate it. In a similar way the warbler-like finch would, at least in its intermediate stages, have been less efficient than a true warbler.

Darwin's finches may well have been the first land birds to arrive on the Galapagos. The islands would have provided an unusual number of diverse, and vacant, environmental niches in which the birds could settle and differentiate. The same may have been true of Hawaii. In my opinion, however, the type of evolution that has occurred in those two groups of islands is not unique. Similar developments could have taken place very long ago on the continents; thus our own finches, warblers and woodpeckers may have evolved from a common ancestor on the mainland. What is unique about the Galapagos and Hawaii is that the birds' evolution there occurred so recently that we can still see the evidence of the differentiations.

Much more is still to be learned from the finches. Unfortunately the wonderful opportunities they offer may not long remain available. Already one of the finches Darwin found in the Galapagos is extinct, and so are several other animals peculiar to the islands. With man have come hunters, rats, dogs and other predators. On some islands men and goats are destroying the native vegetation. This last is the most serious threat of all to Darwin's finches. Unless we take care, our descendants will lose a treasure which is irreplaceable.

THE END OF THE MOAS

by Edward S. Deevey, Jr.

ANY BIOGEOGRAPHER would cheerfully suffer shipwreck on a land as interesting as that of the Swiss Family Robinson. The peccary, ostrich, hyena and walrus disported there with the jackal, buffalo and wild ass, while honey guides and swifts which built edible nests darted among the vanilla and euphorbia trees. In the world of real life there is an island that can vie with the Robinsons' fictional wonderland. It is New Zealand, where three quarters of the plants are peculiar specimens that live nowhere else on earth, where cycads and tree ferns, refugees from Paleozoic coal swamps, grow in sight of active glaciers; where astonishing varieties of flightless birds scurry through the underbrush like rabbits and not long ago grazed the plains like herds of antelope. Indeed, because there are no mammals to prey on them (the only mammals on the island are bats), even geese and perching birds in New Zealand have forsaken the use of their wings.

The weirdest of all the flightless birds of that island were a now extinct kind called moas, which lived in New Zealand for so long a time that they lost their wings entirely. All of them were large and some were gigantic; one variety, *Dinornis*, was a giraffe-like creature ten feet tall. Probably they were not fierce, for they were grazing animals. Mystery surrounds their disappearance. Moa bones and feathers today are found lying on the floors of caves or only a few inches below the surface in swamps. Obviously their extinction was not a remote event.

When, in 1840, the great English anatomist Sir Richard Owen first described these "struthious birds," Europeans assumed that such spectacular creatures must have been known to the aboriginal Maori. Their leading questions to the natives about the birds brought the answers the Maori thought were desired. By 1870 New Zealand folklore was full of circumstantial accounts of moas —how they buried their heads in the sand, how they flapped their wings when they ran, how the female sat on a clutch of thirty eggs while the male stood guard, how the birds were ambushed as they left the caves where they lived.

Sophisticated modern anthropologists, among them Roger Duff, director of the Canterbury Museum at Christchurch, do not believe all they are told by elderly and compliant Maori. That the aborigines knew fossil moas there is no doubt, for they used the bones for artifacts, and the word *moa* itself before 1840 seems to have meant only "a stone; also the name of a person or a place." But apart from a few vague allusions to events which antedated the arrival of the Great Fleet from Tahiti about 1350 and which probably refer in any case to other kinds of birds, there is no authentic record in Maori folklore of their having had any personal acquaintance with living moas. This only deepens the mystery. The moas were there in abundance not more than a few thousand years ago, and had been there for at least twelve million years; if the Maori didn't exterminate them, who did?

Archaeological studies, most recently at Wairau on the northeast coast of the South Island, have supplied a partial answer. Diggings directed by Duff have shown that there was a pre-Maori people who hunted moas. Not only are the birds' great bones found in profusion in middens, but moa eggs, perforated at one end, were buried intact with the dead. No doubt the eggs were used as water bottles, as the South African Bushmen use ostrich eggs, and they were interred with other cherished property of the dead for the journey to the hereafter.

These moa hunters of the South Island may have been the people who exterminated the moas. Certainly they killed the birds in large numbers. Their camp, which was situated at the end of a peninsula, was admirably suited as a cul-de-sac for rounding up moas. Yet this can be only part of the story of the end of the moas. The principal genus found in the camp, *Euryapteryx*, seems to have been designed by nature to become extinct—the savages must have found it a veritable schmoo. Constructed with a slender head and neck and an incredibly massive body below, it was a cross between a hogshead and a gazelle—four times as tall as a domestic chicken and probably ten times as stupid. A few fossils of two other kinds of moas, of about the same size, have been found in the moa hunters' camps. But of Dinornis, the avian giraffe, there is not a trace. Yet Dinornis and Euryapteryx were contemporaries, at least as the geologist views time, and their remains are found together in swamps. The puzzling question changes slightly then: instead of asking "Who killed the moas?" we wonder "Where did Dinornis go?"

The answer is not in yet, but it is within sight as a result of geologic studies at the latest and most important of the moa-bearing swamps to be discovered. This is in Pyramid Valley, about 100 miles inland from Wairau on South Island. Here the moa-trap was an old lake deposit, exceptionally sticky and treacherous. Today it is covered with sedge tussocks and is used as pasture, but when the moas flourished it was a swampy forest into which the ponderous birds were tempted while feeding. Once they broke through its deceptive crust of black forest humus, they were irretrievably mired in the sticky clay beneath, which went down for five or six feet. The long legs of Dinornis were not quite long enough to reach firm bottom, and the smaller species never had a chance. As they floundered, sinking deeper with every struggle, the moas were attacked from above by the giant harpy eagle—so one infers, at least, from the fact that the heads and necks are usually missing from otherwise complete skeletons. Moreover, a few of the eagles themselves were trapped, along with some 30 other kinds of smaller birds.

Excavations in the Pyramid Valley swamp led by Duff and the ornithologist Robert Falla had by 1949 dug out more or less complete skeletons of 140 moas, representing four of the six genera and six of the 20 species found in New Zealand. Forty-four of these skeletons were Dinornis and only 12 Euryapteryx. There were no chicks among them, but one five-foot hen was caught carrying a fully-formed egg with a capacity of more than half a gallon.

Dating the Pyramid Valley swamp is a complicated process. New Zealand bogs, like bogs in other countries, preserve a time-scale in the form of varied assemblages of pollen grains, originally airborne from plants in the neighborhood and fossilized in the accumulating bog sediments. The scale is purely relative, telling the comparative but not the absolute ages of the deposits. Pollen times, established by counting different kinds of pollen in successive layers of bog mud, are converted to climatic times by inference from the nature of the vegetation they record. Because changes of climate operate over wide areas, it is comparatively easy to match up pollen records from bogs a few miles apart. This has been done in great detail in areas in western Europe and eastern North America, where the plants and the climate are fairly uniform. It is not so easy to carry pollen times with any assurance across the North Atlantic Ocean, or from the Northern Hemisphere to the Southern, for purposes of comparative dating.

New Zealand's pollen time-scale was worked out by Lucy Cranwell in collaboration with the inventor of the pollen dating method, Lennart von Post of Stockholm. Applied to Pyramid Valley, it suggests that the marly lake deposit in which the moas were entombed corresponds to the latest of three climatic stages. It was a time when southern beechwoods spread at the expense of coniferous forests, which means that the period was cooler and at first moister than the one that preceded it. A layer of peat containing sedges underlies the marl, and this can be dated to the coniferous-forest period itself. In terms of the Northern Hemisphere time-scale, it can be guessed that the southern-beech time was the same climatic period that saw the expansion of beeches over western Europe at the expense of oaks and lime trees. This happened at the end of the Bronze Age, so that a date of 600 B.C. for the laying down of the marl deposit seems reasonable. The overgrowth of the Pyramid Valley lake by swamp forest should then correspond to one of the later times of dry climate in western Europe, of which the best known fell in the fifth and the thirteenth centuries. If pollen dating is possible over such enormous distances, the moas of Pyramid Valley met their sticky end some time between the fall of Rome and the rise of Italian painting.

If pollen dating is possible over such enormous distances—geology and the other historical sciences are bedeviled by such questions. Geologic happenings are dated in terms of each other, and one can get just so far by matching independent sequences; sooner or later the method fails. It is for this situation that radiocarbon dating seems to be made to order, for its scale of time is measured in absolute terms of centuries or years. In this method the age of a fossilized animal or plant is measured by the decay of radioactive carbon 14 in its tissues since its death.

The most interesting radiocarbon date for Pyramid Valley, as measured in Yale's Geochronometric Laboratory, is not the age of a moa, but that of the peat that underlies the lake deposit in which the moas drowned. This peat proves to be 3,700 years old, a figure which seems about right if the coniferous forest time in New Zealand was the dry time of the European Bronze Age. In other words, pollen dating *can* be carried across enormous distances, and when a few more such dates are measured in both Northern and Southern Hemispheres, we may say that the relative pollen time-scale has been "calibrated." The marly lake deposit itself is older than the moas and younger than the peat, but its radiocarbon dates are mainly useful in proving what had been suspected—that dates based on the carbon of marl (a clay containing calcium carbonate) are less reliable than those for peat.

And what about the moa? The last meal of a large Dinornis consisted of about a bushel of seeds and twigs, found buried in the lake mud along with the skeleton (and a peck of gizzard stones, some as large as a hen's egg). The food remains are woody; when burned and analyzed for radiocarbon, they gave an age of 670 years. Thus we learn that Dinornis roamed New Zealand as recently as about 1300, in company with Euryapteryx. The moa hunters of Wairau may not have exterminated Dinornis, but it certainly seems likely that the people who did wipe out the moas lived not long before these hunters.

Until Dinornis remains are actually found in middens, alternative hypotheses may be preferred by some. Perhaps, like Friedrich Barbarossa, the greatest of the moas is not extinct but merely sleeping. Or perhaps Dinornis, maddened with grief at the death of Euryapteryx, sought Ophelia's melancholy fate. Once a hen Dinornis ventured into Pyramid Valley,

> *". . . long it could not be*
> *Till that her garments, heavy with their drink,*
> *Pull'd the poor wretch from her melodious lay*
> *To muddy death."*

PART 5 PHYSIOLOGICAL ENGINEERING

I. THE METABOLISM OF HUMMING-BIRDS
by Oliver P. Pearson

II. SHREWS
by Oliver P. Pearson

With a 1947 Ph.D. from Harvard University, Oliver P. Pearson joined the Museum of Vertebrate Zoology at the University of California where he is now assistant professor of zoology and assistant curator of mammals. He was drawn to zoology by the influence of a teacher at Swarthmore College, Robert Enders, and declares that he is "still coasting on the impetus received from Enders." He has done field work on both continents of the Western Hemisphere.

III. THE DESERT RAT
by Knut and Bodil Schmidt-Nielsen

A graduate student of the late August Krogh, author of another chapter in this book, Knut Schmidt-Nielsen married his mentor's daughter, Bodil. Knut was born in Trondheim, Norway, in 1915 and educated at the universities of Oslo and Copenhagen. Bodil was born in Copenhagen in 1918, and holds a dental degree and a Ph.D. in physiology. The Schmidt-Nielsens came to the U. S. in 1946 and are now at Duke University, where Knut is professor of zoology and Bodil is assistant professor. At the UNESCO Arid Lands Conference in New Mexico last summer, they presented a report on water metabolism in camels, the product of a joint Guggenheim fellowship.

THE METABOLISM OF HUMMINGBIRDS

by Oliver P. Pearson

THE LIVING RATE of an animal depends on its size: the smaller the animal, the faster it lives. This does not necessarily mean that its life span is shorter (a man is smaller than a horse), but pound for pound the more diminutive animal eats more food, consumes more oxygen, produces more energy—in short, has a higher rate of metabolism. Each gram of mouse tissue, for example, metabolizes much faster and uses much more oxygen per minute than each gram of an elephant's tissues. If the elephant's cells were to live at the pace set by mouse cells, the ponderous animal would be unable to dissipate the resulting heat rapidly enough. It would perish within a few minutes from overheating.

Life has been compared to the flame of a candle. The candle's wax combines with oxygen from the air and produces heat and carbon dioxide. The rate at which the flame burns can be measured by any of these four factors: its consumption of wax or oxygen or its production of heat or carbon dioxide. Similarly, one can measure how "alive" an animal is, how intense are its life processes, by determining how fast it consumes food or oxygen or how fast it produces heat or carbon dioxide. For practical reasons the easiest and most satisfactory yardstick is oxygen consumption. Such measurements have been made on a host of animals from protozoa to mice to elephants.

We are interested here in the small end of the scale. Among the warm-blooded animals about the smallest is the hummingbird—some species of hummingbirds weigh no more than a dime.

As we should expect, the hummingbird has the highest rate of metabolism of any bird or mammal. In a resting hummingbird each gram of tissue metabolizes 15 times as fast as a gram of pigeon and more than 100 times as fast as a gram of elephant. When the metabolism rates of various animals are plotted on a chart, the curve goes up steeply at the small-animal end, and it indicates that at 2.5 grams the rate of metabolism would be infinitely rapid. No bird or mammal so small could exist without resorting to

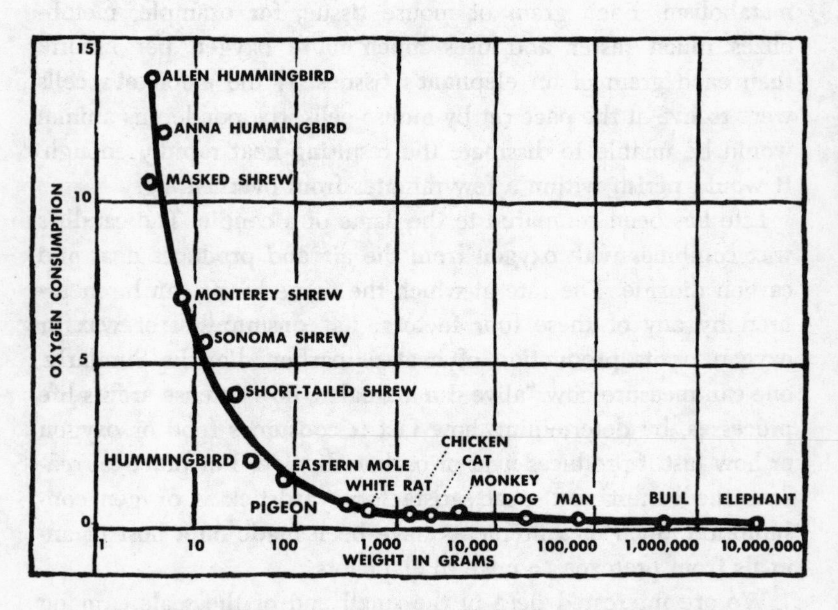

Metabolic relationship of small and large birds and mammals is shown by plotting their oxygen consumption against their weight. The oxygen consumption is given in cubic centimeters per gram per hour.

some metabolic legerdemain unknown to its larger relatives, for it simply could not eat fast enough to avoid starvation.

The hummingbird wins the honor of living at a rate faster than any other animal at the cost of an enormous food consumption. The bird must devote much of its day to gathering food, mainly nectar and insects. But what happens at night? Hummingbirds are not adapted for night feeding. If their intense metabolism continued undiminished through the night, as it does in other birds, they would be in danger of starving to death before morning.

The trick by which hummingbirds avoid overnight starvation was disclosed by means of a continuous record of their oxygen consumption over a 24-hour period. Each hummingbird was confined in a bell jar with a food supply in a vial. During the afternoon the bird alternately perched and hovered in front of its feeding vial. For an hour before nightfall it indulged in intensive feeding, and much flying and wing-buzzing. During that hour it consumed 24 cubic centimeters of oxygen per gram of body weight. Then the bird settled down for the night. Twenty minutes later its rate of metabolism had dropped to eight cubic centimeters per gram per hour. By the middle of the night the bird was living at a metabolism level only one fifteenth as rapid as the daytime rate.

Now this is the level at which certain mammals hibernate. The hummingbird at night showed many signs of hibernation. It was completely torpid, practically insensible, scarcely able to move, and when it did stir, it moved as though congealed. Its body temperature had dropped to that of the surrounding air—75 degrees Fahrenheit. Hibernation, then, is the metabolic magic by which hummingbirds stretch their food stores from dusk to dawn.

Before daybreak the bird's body spontaneously returns to its normal temperature and high metabolic rate. By early morning it is again warm, awake, ready to dart off in search of food.

That hummingbirds behave in the same way in nature as they did in my bell jars was proved by examining them in their natural roosts. One hummingbird of the Anna species was watched while it settled down to sleep at dusk on a tree branch. When I returned to it at 3. A.M., it was completely torpid and allowed itself to be picked off like a ripe fruit. Most hummingbirds live in the tropics.

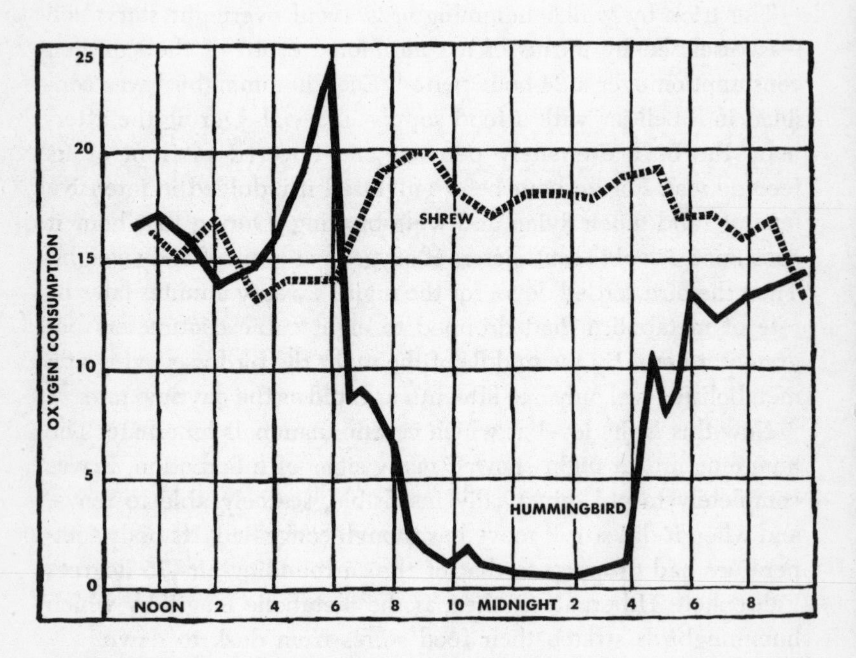

Metabolic rates of a hummingbird and a masked shrew were recorded for 24 hours. The two animals have about the same weight and use oxygen at about the same rate during the day. At night, however, the body temperature of the hummingbird drops almost to that of the surrounding air. This represents a considerable metabolic economy for the 24-hour period. The oxygen consumption is given in cubic centimeters per gram per hour.

A few are found in the high Andes, where temperatures fall so low at night that the birds would probably freeze to death if they stayed in the open air; there they retreat at night into caves.

We know of no other bird that hibernates overnight like the hummingbird. Bats, which are not birds but mammals, do the trick in reverse: they forage by night and slow to torpor by day.

The metabolic profit which a hummingbird gains by nocturnal hibernation can be measured by comparing it with a tiny mammal of about the same size—the shrew *Sorex cinereus*. When they are awake and going about their business in the bell jar, the shrew and the hummingbird have about the same rate of oxygen consumption. But the shrew cannot hibernate. It must keep busy most of the night feeding itself.

When the hummingbird is not sleeping, it is eating, and it does this entirely on the wing. How strenuous is it for a bird to fly? Hummingbirds can hover in a small space, and this attribute makes them ideal subjects for investigation in laboratory confinement.

A bird is put into the bell jar, and the jar is entirely submerged in a large tank of water to ensure a constant temperature. The bird sits quietly on its perch while a continuous record of its rate of metabolism is being made on a smoked drum. After ten or fifteen minutes the bird becomes hungry, flies up to the feed vial suspended near the top of the bell jar, hovers there while feeding, then returns to the perch. The observer times the flight with a stop watch. From the continuous metabolic record he can easily calculate the comparative rates of metabolism during rest and flight.

On the average a small hummingbird consumes somewhere around 80 cubic centimeters of oxygen per gram per hour while hovering. This is about six times its resting rate. The British physiologist A. V. Hill once calculated that a man walking at five miles per hour uses six and a half times as much oxygen as he does when standing still. It is reasonable to say, therefore, that a hummingbird works as hard when it hovers as a man does when he walks rapidly.

James L. G. Fitzpatrick, an engineer associated with the Institute of Aeronautical Sciences in New York, has calculated that hovering hummingbirds consume about 726 British thermal units of energy per pound per hour. This figure, interestingly enough, is very close to the energy consumption of a modern helicopter—750 B.T.U. per pound per hour.

How much energy does a hummingbird spend when flying about? We do not know exactly, but probably it takes somewhat less work than hovering. Like an airplane, a bird probably gains some lift from its forward motion and thus does not have to spend so much energy to stay aloft. At very slow speeds the lift would be negligible, and at very high speeds it would be more than offset by resistance. Between these extremes, however, there is probably a speed range in which birds use less energy to fly forward than they do to hover in one place.

Our laboratory findings may have a bearing on a puzzle which has long mystified ornithologists. The ruby-throated hummingbird spends its summers in the eastern U. S. and its winters in Central America. How does it get across the Gulf of Mexico in its annual migrations? One school holds that it must fly around the shoreline, arguing that it is ridiculous to think that this tiny bird, with its exceedingly high rate of metabolism, could carry enough fuel to make a nonstop flight across the Gulf. On the other hand, many people have repeatedly seen flights of hummers head out over the Gulf, and they insist the birds must be able to make the trip, for they would not set out on a flight which was certain to be fatal.

In the face of two such unthinkable alternatives, any laboratory answer may seem foolish. But we can at least attempt a calculation, if only for the amusement of playing with the figures.

Let us assume that the hummingbirds cruise at 50 m.p.h., the speed at which they have been timed by automobiles. At this speed they might consume 80 cubic centimeters of oxygen per gram per hour. A three-gram ruby-throated hummingbird (the average weight) would burn 240 cubic centimeters of oxygen per hour, and in doing so would release 1.17 calories of heat. Now we can assume that the bird might carry one gram of fat as reserve fuel, for a fat bird of this species is about one gram heavier than a lean one. One gram of fat yields nine calories. Consequently the bird could fly 7.7 hours on its fat (9 divided by 1.17). At 50 m.p.h., this would carry it 385 miles. Impressive though the figure is, it does not get the hummingbird to shore. The shortest distance across the Gulf is more than 500 miles.

It may be argued that because of the crudity of some of our assumptions, we still have not thrown much light on the subject in dispute. Perhaps we have contributed only more heat, but if so, at least it can be measured in calories.

SHREWS

by Oliver P. Pearson

TO MOST PEOPLE a shrew is a vexatious, scolding, turbulent woman tamed over and over again in theatrical productions since the time of Shakespeare. To a biologist a shrew is a vexatious, scolding, turbulent mammal (order of insect eaters) that has rarely submitted to taming since long before Shakespeare. Because shrews are extremely tiny, live in burrows and seldom interfere with man's interests and activities, even their unruly personality has failed to bring them to people's attention. Their obscurity is certainly not due to scarcity; in the eastern third of the U. S., for instance, probably the most abundant mammal is a certain species of shrew. More than thirty species are found in North America, and the animal makes its home on every major continent except Australia.

The American shrews resemble small moles (to which they are related) and earless mice (no relation). They have long, pointed noses, tiny eyes and velvety fur. Some of them are astonishingly small, weighing less than a penny. The shrew's plushlike fur is well suited to its life in burrows, for no matter in which direction the animal goes its hair does not muss. Its eyes are almost hidden in its fur. It has little need of them, as a matter of fact, for it spends practically all of its time in dark tunnels or thick vegetation, where it must rely primarily on hearing (which is good despite its negligible ear lobes), on smell and on tactile stimuli, received by sensitive whiskers near the tip of its nose. Shrews move about constantly, quivering their nose nervously and sometimes keeping up a faint, thin, high-pitched twittering. Some individuals of the common short-tailed species when cornered throw their head back, open their mouth and utter a long, shrill chatter that sounds like the song of the Tennessee warbler.

The shrew's living requirements are moisture, cover and a supply of small invertebrates and seeds for food. It is so small that it can make its home in leaf-mold grass, sphagnum or marsh plants, where it digs a tunnel or makes a leafy nest. It lives in such diverse environments as forests, meadows, bogs and salt marshes. Shrews like deciduous forests that are rich in leaf litter and rotting logs. Rolling aside one of these logs frequently discloses a shrew tunnel or nest. The little animal finds plenty of worms, grubs and insects within its tunnel and runways, but it must also scurry out at frequent intervals for nuts and seeds to fill out its diet.

So elusive are shrews that even experienced investigators seldom see them in the wild. About the only way to get a look at them is to capture them in mousetraps. Traps placed at their runways and other favorable spots will catch a fair number, but the captures give no true idea of the actual shrew population, for some of the species are trap-shy. I trapped for many years in suburban Philadelphia, using all sorts of ingenious (I thought) traps, without catching a single shrew of the species *Cryptotis parva*. Yet I discovered that barn owls were catching these little shrews in the same area. The first specimens of Cryptotis ever found in Canada were discovered (still alive) in the stomach of a milk snake. Some years ago Marcus Lyon, an Indiana mammalogist, reported that in many years of trapping he had captured only one Cryptotis in that state. But on Christmas Day 1949, a hawk shot in Wayne County, Indiana, had in its digestive system the remains of twenty-seven Cryptotis!

Shrews are noted for their nervous restlessness, and there is good reason for this. As the smallest living mammals, they have the highest rate of metabolism, for the "living" rate of animal tissue goes up as animal size goes down, as indicated in the chart on page 94. One of the smaller species of shrew, *Sorex cinereus*, metabolizes four times as fast as a mouse per gram of tissue. To support their high rate of metabolism shrews must devour enormous quantities of food. To be impressed by the appetite of the shrew, you need only capture one and try to keep it fed. You will soon weary of any attempt to catch enough worms, grubs and insects to satiate it and will have to resort to teaching the shrew to eat dog food and ground meat. One man found that his 3.6-gram Sorex consumed in eight days more than 93 grams of food—earthworms, rolled oats, mice, sow bugs, grasshoppers, snails, fish and whatnot. The shrew ate on the average 3.3 times its own weight per day. C. Hart Merriam, a pioneer American mammalogist, once confined three Sorex under a glass tumbler. Two of them promptly attacked and devoured the third. Eight hours later only a single shrew, with slightly bulging stomach, remained. The tiny cannibal had transmuted both of its companions into a small heap of droppings and a few calories of wasted heat.

Such voracity is ordinarily directed toward small invertebrates, but *Blarina*, one of the larger shrews, frequently eats mice two or three times its own size. It readily kills big meadow mice. A. F. Shull, a member of the famous family of Midwest biologists, once found a Blarina nest made exclusively of mouse hair. Beside this nest were two freshly killed meadow mice and the body of a third half-eaten, and nearby lay several handfuls of hair in which were mixed the legs and tails of about 20 more. Shull was prompted to attempt an estimate of the predatory impact of shrews on meadow mice. Assuming that mice made up about 40 per cent of the diet of these shrews, he calculated that each shrew would consume about eight mice per month. Figuring a population of four shrews per acre, on a 100-acre farm the total number of mice consumed by shrews in a year would be 38,400!

Such "headlong" statistics are frequently full of pitfalls, but in this case may not be far misleading. Recent studies by Robert

Eadie, a Cornell zoologist, support Shull's conclusions, if not his statistics. Eadie, like other collectors, had frequently been humiliated by having shrews invade his mousetraps and escape, leaving their droppings on the floor. Making the best of this frustrating discovery, he left large numbers of paper squares about to collect shrew droppings, usually hard to find. After analyzing the content of the droppings over many seasons, he concluded that Blarina shrews catch large numbers of meadow mice, even in years when the mice are scarce, and probably are important regulators of the meadow-mouse population.

Blarina possesses a venom that helps to subdue its prey. As far as we know it is the only mammal with a poisonous bite, although some European and African shrews are suspected also. Its venom is powerful enough to kill a human being if injected into the bloodstream, but the animal lacks an effective injection mechanism. Unlike poisonous snakes, it has no hollow fangs; the poison seeps into its bite from a groove between its long lower incisor teeth. This mechanism seems to be adequate to kill a mouse but not an animal as large as a rabbit.

Nonetheless, European folklore is full of references to the toxicity of shrews and to spectacular remedies applied to people bitten or bewitched by them. One account appears in a fascinating compendium by a seventeenth-century clergyman named Edward Topsell, entitled *The History of Four-footed Beasts and Serpents: describing at large their true and lively Figure, their several Names, Conditions, Kinds, Virtues (both Natural and Medicinal), Countries of their Breed, their Love and Hatred to Mankind, and the wonderful work of God in their Creation, Preservation, and Destruction. Interwoven with curious variety of Historical Narrations out of Scriptures, Fathers, Philosophers, Physicians, and Poets: Illustrated with divers Hieroglyphicks and Emblems, &c., both pleasant and profitable for Students in all Faculties and Professions.* Concerning shrews the reverend wrote:

"It is a ravening Beast, feigning itself gentle and tame, but, being touched, it biteth deep, and poysoneth deadly . . . There is nothing which do more apparently explain and shew the biting of a Shrew then a certain vehement pain and grief in the creature which is so bitten, as also a pricking over the whole body, with an inflammation or burning heat going round about the place, and a fiery redness therein, in which a black push or like swelling with a watery matter, and filthy corruption doth arise, and all parts of the body which do joyn unto it seem black and blew with the marvellous great pain, anguish, and grief, which ariseth and proceedeth from the same."

In 1889 a New England naturalist, C. J. Maynard, also reported, though less vividly, the effects of a bite on the hand while he was trying to capture a Blarina shrew. His skin was slightly punctured in a number of places. Within thirty seconds he felt a burning sensation, and soon afterward shooting pains ran up his arm. The pain and swelling reached a maximum in about an hour. He could not use his hand without great suffering for three days and felt considerable discomfort for more than a week afterward. His report of the incident was published in an obscure journal at a time when Pasteur's work on rabies and "microbes" held the center of attention. Sophisticated scientists of the day attributed Maynard's symptoms to microbes and dismissed the idea that the shrew had injected a poison.

Actual proof of the toxicity of shrews came only a few years ago. In the course of a joint reconnaissance of the microscopic anatomy of the common short-tailed shrew of the eastern U. S., George Wislocki, eminent anatomist of the Harvard Medical School, pointed out to me an unusual group of cells in the microscopic tubules of the shrew's submaxillary salivary glands (below the lower jaw). It seemed worth while to test these cells as a possible source of venom. Extracts from the glands, made by grinding them in salt solution, were injected into mice. They proved highly lethal to the mice. In fact, only one 200th of the submaxillary extract from a single Blarina will kill a white mouse within a few minutes when injected into its bloodstream. The gross symptoms are labored breathing, protruding eyes and convulsions.

Some standard pharmacological tests were then applied to cats and rabbits with the help of Otto Krayer, professor of pharmacology at the Harvard Medical School. The shrew venom had a dramatic effect on the heartbeat, blood pressure and respiration of the animals. A three-pound rabbit succumbed in less than five minutes to an intravenous injection of extract from only ten milligrams of submaxillary tissue. One shrew provides more than seven times this much venom. There seems little doubt that the venom could kill a human being if injected intravenously.

Despite their abundance shrews are not exceptionally prolific. A female of the short-tailed species, for example, has no more than two or three litters in a year—one or two in the spring and, if she survives, another in the summer. The average size of the litter is around five. Females born in the spring mature rapidly and soon can reproduce, but those born in the autumn do not reproduce until the following spring.

In captivity shrews can live more than two and a half years. In the wild, however, they age rapidly and encounter so many hazards that few live to be a year old. Among a sample of short-tailed shrews marked and released in the summer only a little more than 6 per cent survived until the following summer. And since a large number of young perish even before they are weaned or are old enough to be caught, marked and released, it is safe to say that the life expectancy of a shrew at birth is not more than a few months. Survival of the species is left to the immature, inexperienced generation that lives over the winter—a situation reminiscent of many species of insects, whose adults perish by the end of the season and entrust the preservation of the race entirely to larvae and pupae.

There has been some dispute about whether shrews die more commonly of old age or of violence. The facts that their tissues live at a rapid rate and that the uneaten bodies of dead shrews are sometimes found lying about in the woods and fields (more often than the bodies of dead mice) seem to suggest that many die of old age. However, nearly all the shrew carcasses I have found have shown clear evidence, beneath their fur, of a violent death. A record of the age distributions of samples of the shrew population trapped in various months of the year shows a high attrition among all groups, young and old, as the year goes on.

The simplest explanation of the carcasses found in nature is that shrews are unpalatable to many predators. They have powerful scent glands in the skin. The short-tailed shrew gives forth a particularly offensive odor from oily skin glands on each side and along the midline of the belly. The odor seems to become stronger when the shrews are excited or angry. It renders shrews less palatable to foxes, cats, weasels and probably to many other animals that prey on shrews. It offers no protection against hawks or owls, however, because they have no sense of smell.

In the Blarina genus of shrews, females in the breeding stage have less well-developed scent glands than the rest of the population. This is rather surprising, because for the sake of the population those females are the most in need of protection against predators. Probably the answer is that the scent glands also serve another purpose—a social one. A wandering male shrew encountering an unscented runway or tunnel may assume that it is either vacant or occupied by a breeding female, and so not hesitate to enter. On the other hand, males are heavily scented during the breeding season. The scent, rubbing off on their burrows, may serve both to attract breeding females and as a keep-out sign to others. Birds use song in the same way, and male dogs stake territorial claims by scenting tree trunks and other objects.

One of the most interesting and unusual shrews is a water species (*Sorex palustris*) which lives along cold streams in mountainous parts of the U. S. and in Canada. It catches fish and aquatic insect larvae under water and is an excellent swimmer, propelling itself with long alternate strokes of its big hind feet plus some assistance from its front paws. On the surface it can swim at about two feet per second, and when startled or under water it appears to go much faster. It can leap at least its own body length out of the water. Streaking past a trout fisherman's feet under water, it looks like a mercury-coated mouse, for its fur traps a silvery film of air. It seldom stays under water for more than a few seconds, but even this brief holding of its breath is impressive in an animal which normally breathes several hundred times per minute.

Konrad Lorenz, in his charming book about animals, *King Solomon's Ring,* tells of a family of captive European water shrews which memorized a particular pathway in their cage. They scurried unhesitatingly along this path, like a locomotive on its track, until some minor rearrangement was made in the pathway, whereupon the shrews were thrown into confusion. At one point on the route the shrews were accustomed to jump onto a pile of small stones and then off the other side. When the stones were removed, shrews coming along the path jumped into the air at the appropriate place but landed on the floor of the cage with a disconcerting bump. Then, despite the fact that their vision is good enough to see obstructions, the shrews made their way back onto the accustomed pathway and with restored confidence repeated the pointless leap. Although this behavior appears to demonstrate gross stupidity, it should be pointed out in the shrew's favor that its remarkable path-memory normally releases its other senses for more important activities. Its substitution of habit for reason may seem unenlightened to us, but the abundance and success of shrews throughout the world are strong evidence that in the shrew's case the substitution is effective.

THE DESERT RAT

by Knut and Bodil Schmidt-Nielsen

THERE IS a common impression that no higher animal can live long without drinking water. Certainly this is true of man and many other mammals; we need water at frequent intervals, and in a very hot, dry desert a man without water cannot last more than a day or so. An animal such as the camel can survive somewhat longer, but sooner or later it too must drink to refill its supply.

Yet we know that the waterless desert is not uninhabited. Even in desert areas with no visible drinking water within scores of miles, one will often find a fairly rich animal life. How do these animals get the water they must have to live? The body of a desert mammal has about the same water content (65 per cent of body weight) as that of a drinking animal, and it generally has no more tolerance to desiccation of the tissues, sometimes less. For many desert animals the answer is simple: they get their water in their food. These animals live on juicy plants, one of the most important of which is cactus. The pack rat, for example, eats large quantities of cactus pulp, which is about 90 per cent water. Thus it is easy to account for the survival of animals in areas where cacti and other water-storing plants are available.

There are, however, animals which can live in areas altogether barren of juicy vegetation. An outstanding example is a certain general type of desert rodent which is found in all the major desert areas of the world—in Africa, in Asia, in Australia and in the southwestern U. S. Although the rats of this type seem to have evolved independently in the several areas and are not related to one another, all of them are similar in appearance and habits and all seem to be able to live with a minimum of water. How they do so has long been a puzzle to biologists.

During the past few years we have investigated intensively a rodent of this type—the so-called kangaroo rat that lives in deserts of the U. S. Southwest. In a field laboratory in Arizona and in biological laboratories at Swarthmore College, Stanford University and the University of Cincinnati we have studied the kangaroo rat's habits and physiology, and we now have a good understanding of how this rodent is able to get along on a diet so dry that other animals would soon die of thirst.

The little kangaroo rat is not actually related to the kangaroo, though it looks a great deal like one. It hops along on long hind legs, and it has a long, strong tail which it uses for support and steering. It lives in a burrow in the ground by day and comes out for food only at night. The animal thrives in the driest regions, even in the bare sand dunes of Death Valley. Water to drink, even dew, is rarely available in its natural habitat. The kangaroo rat apparently has only a short range of movement—not more than a few hundred yards—and therefore does not leave its dry area to find juicy plants. Stomach analyses have shown that it seldom or never consumes any succulent vegetation. Its food consists of seeds and other dry plant material. In the laboratory it will live indefinitely without water and with no other food but dry barley seeds.

The first question to be answered was whether the kangaroo rat stores water in its body to carry it over long dry periods. It was found that the animal's water content was always about the same (some 65 per cent of body weight), in the rainy season or the dry season, or after it had been kept on dry food in the laboratory for several weeks. During eight weeks on nothing but dry barley in the laboratory some of the animals increased their body weight, and their water percentage was as high as at the beginning of the experiment; they had actually increased the total amount of water in their bodies. Furthermore, kangaroo rats which were given watermelon as well as barley to eat showed no higher water percentage in their bodies than animals maintained on a dry diet. They must therefore have eliminated the excess of water at the same rate as it was taken in. Altogether the experiments made clear that the kangaroo rat does not store water or live through dry periods at the expense of its body water.

There is only one way the kangaroo rat can get any substantial amount of water on its dry diet. That is by oxidizing its food. The oxidation of hydrogen or a substance containing hydrogen always forms water. Obviously the amount of water an animal forms in its metabolism will depend upon the hydrogen content of its food. The amount is simply a matter of chemistry and is the same in all animals. Oxidation of a gram of carbohydrate (starch or sugar) yields .6 of a gram of water; of a gram of fat, 1.1 grams of water; of a gram of protein, .3 of a gram of water. Protein produces relatively little water because a considerable part of its hydrogen is not oxidized but is excreted with nitrogen as urea.

Now the experimental diet of dry barley on which the kangaroo rats lived yields 54 grams of water for each 100 grams of barley (dry weight) consumed. If there is any moisture in the air, the barley will also contain a little absorbed water—about 13 grams per 100 grams when the relative humidity is 50 per cent at 75 degrees Fahrenheit. The kangaroo rat consumes 100 grams of barley in a period of about five weeks. Thus during that period its total intake of water is between 54 and 67 grams, depending on atmospheric conditions.

This is an astonishingly small amount of water for an animal of its size to subsist on. It can maintain its water balance only if its water losses are correspondingly small. The next step, therefore, was to find out how the animal manages to keep its water loss so low, if indeed it does. We proceeded to measure its losses of water through the three routes by which an animal eliminates water; in the urine, in the feces and by evaporation from the skin and the respiratory passages.

There is an animal, the African lungfish, which can get along for long periods without excreting any urine at all. When the stream or pond in which it is living dries up, it burrows into the mud and stays there until the next rain. The eminent authority on the kidney, Homer W. Smith, has found that during this time the urea content of the fish's blood may rise to the extravagant level of 4 per cent. Can the kangaroo rat similarly accumulate waste products and avoid urinating during a dry spell? We investigated and found that it could not: the urea and salt content of its blood did not rise when it was on a dry diet or fall when it had a moist diet. And it continued on its dry diet to excrete urea as usual.

However, we learned that it could get rid of its waste products with a very small output of water. The kangaroo rat has an amazingly efficient kidney. The concentration of urea in its urine can be as high as 24 per cent, whereas in man the maximum is about 6 per cent. Thus the kangaroo rat needs only about one fourth as much water to eliminate a given amount of urea as a man would. Its excretion of salts is similarly efficient. The animal can excrete urine about twice as salty as sea water!

The reason that a human being cannot tolerate drinking sea water is that the body is dehydrated in the process of getting rid of the salts. The saltiness of the kangaroo rat's urine suggested that this animal might be able to drink sea water and get a net water gain from it. Of course it was not easy to induce the kangaroo rat, which normally does not drink, to imbibe sea water. But we were able to make it do so by feeding it a high protein diet (soy beans) which formed very large amounts of urea and forced the rat to drink to avoid dehydration. The animal's kidney proved able to excrete both the excess of urea and the salts in the sea water. Drinking sea water actually enabled the animal to maintain its water balance. So far as is known, no other mammal can drink sea water with impunity.

From the known efficiency of the kangaroo rat's kidney we calculated that the animal uses 13 grams of water to excrete the waste products formed from 100 grams of dry barley. Measurement of the water content of its feces, which are exceptionally dry, showed that it loses about three grams of water by this route in metabolizing 100 grams of dry barley. There remained, then, the question of how much water the kangaroo rat loses by evaporation.

Very little escapes through its skin. Rodents have no sweat glands except on the toe pads, and the kangaroo rat has fewer sweat glands than most rats. All mammals lose a little water from the skin even where there are no sweat glands, and there is reason to believe that the kangaroo rat suffers less loss by this route than other mammals. It does, however, lose a considerable amount of water by evaporation from its respiratory tract. In the extremely dry desert air this loss could be serious. At zero humidity the loss by evaporation from the skin and respiratory tract would amount to some 44 grams of water during the five weeks in which the rat metabolizes 100 grams of barley. At a relative humidity of 50 per cent and a temperature of 75 degrees the loss by evaporation would be about 25 grams.

We can now add up the balance sheet of the kangaroo rat's water intake and outgo. At zero humidity its total intake on a diet of dry barley would be 54 grams, and the total loss would be 61 grams (14 in the urine, 3 in the feces and 44 by evaporation). At 50 per cent relative humidity at 75 degrees the intake would be 67 grams and the outgo only 43 grams. Thus it seems clear that the kangaroo rat cannot survive on a barley diet in completely dry air, for under those conditions it has a water deficit in spite of its marvelous mechanisms for water conservation. Actual tests showed that the minimum atmospheric conditions under which the animal can maintain its water balance on the dry diet is 10 to 20 per cent relative humidity at 75 degrees.

The desert atmosphere is often somewhat drier than this, but the explanation of the kangaroo rat's survival is that it is a night animal. During the day it stays in its burrow, where the air is always a little more humid than outside, even when the soil seems to be completely dry. To measure the temperature and humidity in the burrow we used a tiny instrument which included a humidity-sensitive hair hygrometer. The instrument makes a record on a smoked glass disk, which can be read afterward under a microscope. The recorder was tied to the rat's tail, and the animal dragged it into the burrow. It was secured by a thin wire so that the animal could not run away with the instrument. After 12 hours we opened the burrow and read the record. We found that in early summer in the Arizona desert the relative humidity inside the kangaroo rat's burrows ranged from 30 to 50 per cent, and the temperature from about 75 to 88 degrees. At night, in the desert outside the burrows, the relative humidity varied from 15 to 40 per cent and the temperature from about 60 to 75 degrees. The protection of the burrow by day provides just enough margin to enable the kangaroo rat to maintain its water balance and live in the driest of our deserts.

The same protection allows the kangaroo rat to survive the desert heat. A mammal such as man avoids overheating only by evaporating large quantities of water. The kangaroo rat cannot do this, nor can it tolerate a body temperature of much more than 100 degrees. It does not sweat or increase evaporation from its respiratory passages by panting, as a dog does. If it were exposed to the daytime heat in the desert, it would soon perish. The adaptations that permit it to thrive in the hot desert are its nocturnal habits and its extraordinary facilities for water conservation.

PART 6 FLIGHT AND NAVIGATION

I. BIRD AERODYNAMICS
by John H. Storer

For twenty-three years after his graduation from Harvard College in 1911 John H. Storer was engaged in the practical genetics of fruit and poultry, developing high production strains. Then the hobby of photography became a full-time interest. This chapter was written out of his own original research with a slow-motion camera, which is accounted more fully in *The Flight of Birds,* published by the Cranbrook Institute of Science. His films on ecology and geology have won prizes and have been shown in theaters and on television. *The Web of Life,* a book about ecology for the layman which he wrote in 1953, was published in paperback edition last autumn.

II. BIRDS AS FLYING MACHINES
by Carl Welty

Carl Welty is professor of zoology and chairman of the biology department at Beloit College in Wisconsin. He got his bachelor's degree at Earlham College, a Quaker school in Indiana, and his master's at Haverford in 1925. His career includes a tour of duty on the faculty of Frontier College, Toronto, as teacher of reading, writing and arithmetic to French-Canadian lumberjacks. Classes began at the close of a full eleven-hour working day, in which teacher worked alongside pupils.

III. THE NAVIGATION OF BIRDS
by Donald R. Griffin

IV. SONAR IN BATS
by Donald R. Griffin

V. SONAR IN BIRDS
by Donald R. Griffin

Professor of zoology at Harvard University, Donald R. Griffin is a specialist in the sensory physiology of animal orientation. Born in 1915, Griffin got his A.B. and Ph.D. at Harvard and spent the war years there working on physiological research for the government. After seven postwar years at Cornell, he returned to Harvard in 1953.

BIRD AERODYNAMICS

by John H. Storer

THE FLIGHT of birds has always excited man's envy and wonder. At first sight the process looks simple enough: a bird seems to lift and drive itself forward by beating its wings against the air in much the same way as a swimmer propels himself through water by flapping his arms. When men first tried to fly, they built their flying machines ("ornithopters") on this principle, with mechanical wings that flapped. But the machines never got off the ground.

For this is not at all the way birds fly. Paradoxically it was the development of the modern propeller plane that finally taught us how birds fly—not the other way around. A bird is actually a living airplane. It flies by the same aerodynamical principles as a plane and uses much of the same mechanical equipment—wings, propellers, steering gear, even slots and flaps for help in taking off and landing.

The slow-motion camera shows that a bird does not push itself along by beating its wings back against the air. On the downstroke the wings move forward, not backward. And when the bird lifts its wings for the next stroke, it does not lose altitude, as might be expected, but sails on steadily on a level course. The easiest way to understand its flight is to consider first how an airplane flies.

The air, like any fluid, has weight, and it presses against every surface of anything submerged in it—downward from above, upward from below and inward from all sides. At sea level the air presses on all surfaces with a force of 14.7 pounds per square inch. The air therefore will supply the force to support flight, provided the flying object can somehow reduce the pressure on its upper surface to less than the lifting pressure, and decrease the pressure against its front surface or increase that from behind. Birds and airplanes do this by means of properly shaped wings and propellers which they manipulate to drive themselves forward at a certain required angle and speed.

We can study the aerodynamical problems involved by blowing a stream of smoke, which makes the air currents visible, against an obstruction in a wind tunnel. When the smoke stream hits the obstruction, it does not flow smoothly around the surface and close up again immediately behind it. Instead, it breaks up and is deflected away from the obstruction so that the air no longer presses against the object's sides with the same force. Moreover, the air stream does not close up again until it has moved some distance past the obstruction, so the pressure on the rear surface of the obstacle also is reduced. There remains a disproportionate pressure on the front surface of the obstacle: what would be known as "drag" if the object instead of the air stream were moving.

Now suppose we place in the air stream an object so shaped that it fills in the spaces that were left vacant when the air was deflected by the first obstruction. The air flows smoothly around this new object, and the pressure is more nearly even on all sides. Drag is reduced. We have "streamlined" the obstacle. By altering this shape just a little, we can change the relative pressures on its different surfaces. Let us flatten the bottom surface slightly, reducing the downward deflection of the air stream. Now the upward pressure of air against the bottom surface is more nearly normal, while the downward pressure on the top surface remains subnormal as before. Presto! We have more pressure from below than from above. If the streamlined model is light enough, the moving air will lift it. We have the beginning of a wing.

If the front edge of this embryo wing is tilted upward just a little so that the air strikes the bottom surface more directly, the lifting force on the wing is increased. The more the wing is tilted, the more lift it will give—up to a certain point. As the angle of tilt approaches the vertical, the pressure against the bottom surface begins to push the wing backward rather than upward. Eventually, if a plane's wing is tilted too much, the lifting force vanishes, the drag is so great that it stops the plane, and we have what is known as a "stall." The plane must regain the proper angle and speed or it will crash.

In the air a pilot controls the lifting power of his plane both by tilt and by speed: the more speed, the more lift. In taking off or landing, however, he must rely mainly on tilt: to get enough lifting force he must hold his wing at the greatest possible angle against the air, up to the point of stalling. The angle to which he can tilt the wing without stalling can be increased by placing a very small auxiliary wing in front of or behind the main wing. The "slot" formed between the main wing and the small auxiliary airfoil increases the speed of the air flow over the wing and so maintains its lifting power, even after it has passed the normal stalling point.

Once we have a streamlined wing, the next step necessary for flying is to move it through the air fast enough to generate lift. This we accomplish by equipping the machine with propellers, which are actually another set of wings, whose "lift" is exerted forward rather than upward. For mechanical reasons the blades of a propeller function better with a shape and angle slightly different from those of the wings, but the principle on which they work is just the same.

So we have, basically, a single mechanism which, placed in one position, holds an airplane up, and in another, drives it forward. Now we can look at a bird's anatomy and find exactly the same mechanism used in just the same two ways.

The wing of a bird consists of two parts, which have two very different functions. It is divided into an inner half, operated from the shoulder joint, and an outer half, which is moved separately by a "wrist" midway along the wing. The inner half of the wing is devoted almost exclusively to giving lift. It is held rather rigidly at a slight angle, sloping like the wing of a plane. It also has the streamlined shape of a plane's wing: its upper feathers are arched to make a curved surface.

At the front edge of the wrist, where the inner and outer wings join, is a small group of feathers called the alula. This is the bird's auxiliary airfoil for help in taking off and landing. The bird can raise the alula to form a slot between that structure and the main wing. Without the alula a bird cannot take off or land successfully.

But where is the propeller? Astonishing as it may seem, every bird has a pair of them, though where they might be is certainly far from obvious. They can be seen in action best in a slow-motion picture of a bird in flight. During the downward beat of the wings the primary feathers at the wing tips stand out almost at right angles to the rest of the wing and to the line of flight. These feathers are the propellers. They take on this twisted form for only a split second during each wing beat. But this ability to change their shape and position is the key to bird flight. Throughout the entire wing beat they are constantly changing their shape, adjusting automatically to air pressure and the changing requirements of the wing as it moves up and down.

This automatic adjustment is made possible by special features of the feather design. The front vane of a wing-tip feather (on the forward side of the quill) is much narrower than the rear vane. Out of this difference comes the force that twists the feather into the shape of a propeller. As the wing beats downward against the air, the greater pressure against the wide rear vane of each of these feathers twists that vane upward until the feather takes on the proper shape and angle to function as a propeller. The degree and shape of its twist is controlled largely by the design of the quill, which is rigid at its base but flattened and flexible toward the end.

With their specialized design the primary feathers are beautifully adapted to meet the varied demands of bird flight. An airplane's propeller rotates around a pivot in one direction; the bird's propeller, in contrast, oscillates rapidly down and up, and it must automatically adapt its shape, position, angle and speed to the changing requirements of the moment. The feathers are not fastened immovably to the bone of the wing but are held by a broad flexible membrane, which allows considerable freedom of movement to each feather. While the bird is flying easily, only the tips of the feathers twist to become propellers. But if the bird is in a hurry and beats its wings more strongly against the air, the whole outer section of the wing, from the wrist out, may be twisted by the greater pressure into one big propeller.

The path of the propeller on the downstroke is downward and forward; on the upstroke, upward and backward. The amount of forward and backward motion varies with the bird's wing beat. When the bird beats its wings fast, as in taking off, the increased pressure drives the wing tips forward on a more nearly horizontal path; in leisurely flight the movement is more nearly vertical. The inner wing, by maintaining the proper angle, supports the bird's weight through the entire wing beat. This angle is constantly adjusted to maintain a steady lifting force.

In free flight the bird's powerful breast muscles sweep the whole wing up and down from the shoulder. The inner wing does not actually need to move, but it acts as a handle to move the propeller and gives the latter greater speed and power. I have a slow-motion movie of a low-flying white heron skimming some bushes so closely that it did not have room to make a full downward wing beat. The bird held the inner half of each wing extended horizontally and beat the outer half up and down from the wrist. To move the propeller fast enough without the help of the breast muscles must have required great effort. But this flight demonstrated perfectly the true function of each half of the wing. The inner half was the wing of a living airplane, lifting the bird. The outer half was the propeller, driving it forward.

Like an airplane, a bird has special equipment for steering and balancing. It steers by turning its tail, up, down or sidewise. (It can also spread the tail wide to give added lifting surface when needed.) The bird balances itself by means of its wings; if it tips to one side, it can restore itself to an even keel by increasing the lift of that wing, either by beating more strongly with it or by changing its angle.

Of all the powers of birds in the air probably none has caused more wonder than their soaring ability. To see a bird rise in the air and sail on motionless wings into the distance until at last it disappears from sight gives one a sense of magic. We now know how it is done, but it is still difficult to realize what is happening as we watch it.

Actually the bird is coasting downhill in relation to the flow of air. It rises because it is riding a rising current of air which is ascending faster than the bird is sinking in the current.

Ascending air currents on which birds can soar or glide arise from two different kinds of situations. One is an obstruction, such as an ocean wave, a shore line or a hillside, which deflects the wind upward. It is common to see a pelican or albatross sailing over the water on motionless wings just above the crest of a moving wave, or a gull hanging motionless against a wind current that rises over a headland, or a hawk soaring on the air current that sweeps up a mountainside.

The second type of rising current is heated air, known as a thermal. A field warmed by the sun heats the air above it, causing it to expand and rise. If the field is surrounded by a cooler forest, the heated pocket of air may rise in the form of a great bubble or of a column. Everyone has seen birds soaring in wide circles over land; usually they are coasting around the periphery of a rising air column. Over the ocean, when the water warms colder air above it, the air rises in a whole group of columns, packed together like the cells of a honeycomb. If the wind then freshens, it may blow the columns over until they lie horizontally on the water. The flat-lying columns of air may rotate around their axes, each in the opposite direction from its neighbor. This has been demonstrated in the laboratory by blowing smoke-filled air over a warmed surface at increasing speed, corresponding to an increase in the wind over the ocean. If you put your two fists together and rotate them, the right clockwise and the left counter-clockwise, you will see that the two inner faces of the fists rise together. Just so two adjoining air cells rotating in opposite directions will push up between them a ridge of rising air. Birds can glide in a straight line along such a ridge.

At the Woods Hole Oceanographic Institution Alfred H. Woodcock studied the soaring of sea gulls at different seasons. During the summer, when the air is warmer than the water, gulls seldom do any soaring. But they do a great deal of it in the fall, when the water is warmer than the air and produces many updrafts. The gull's movements may clearly mark the outlines of the rising air columns. When the wind is relatively light, under 16 miles an hour, the gulls soar in spirals, showing that the columns are standing upright. But as the wind freshens and tilts over the columns, the birds' soaring patterns begin to change; when the wind speed reaches 24 miles per hour, all the gulls soar in straight lines. The spectacle is all but incredible, with the birds sailing into the strong wind on motionless wings and gaining altitude as they go, until they disappear in the distance. I watched it once, and it is a never-to-be-forgotten sight.

How fast do birds fly? A great deal of nonsense has been uttered on this subject. The measurement of a bird's speed capabilities is

	MILES PER HOUR
GREAT BLUE HERON *(CRUISING)*	18-29
GREAT BLUE HERON *(PRESSED)*	36
(CANADA GOOSE *EASY FLIGHT*)	20
CANADA GOOSE *(PRESSED BY PLANE)*	45-60
MALLARD *(PRESSED BY PLANE)*	55-60
DUCK HAWK *(PRESSED BY PLANE)*	175-180
PHEASANT *(AVERAGE TOP SPEED)*	60
WOODCOCK	5-13
RUBY-THROATED HUMMINGBIRD *(EASY FLIGHT)*	45-55
BARN SWALLOW	20-46
CROW	25-60
SHARP-SHINNED HAWK	16-60
OSPREY	20-80

a very uncertain and tricky thing. The wind, the angle of the bird's flight, whether it is being pressed—these factors and many others affect its speed.

The cruising and top speeds of some common birds are listed in the table opposite. Birds vary greatly, of course, in their speed requirements and possibilities. The pheasant and grouse, which have short wings adapted to maneuvering in underbrush, must fly with a rapid wing beat and considerable speed to stay in the air. The same is true of ducks, which do not need large wings because they have an easy landing field on the water. Herons, on the other hand, must be able to land slowly to protect their long, slender legs, which they use for wading to find food. Their big, cumbersome wings are suited for slow landing, but they produce so much friction and drag in the air that herons cannot fly very fast.

As the table shows, 60 miles an hour is fast for a bird, and the fastest known species, the duck hawk, does not exceed 175 to 180 miles per hour. These speeds, of course, are far slower than the speeds of modern planes. They involve very different problems in aerodynamics, and different streamline designs. But some of them do approach the speed of the early planes, and it is interesting to see how closely the designs produced by nature approach the best results of the human engineer.

BIRDS AS FLYING MACHINES

by Carl Welty

THE GREAT STRUGGLE in most animals' lives is to avoid change. A chickadee clinging to a piece of suet on a bitter winter day is doing its unconscious best to maintain its internal status quo. Physiological constancy is the first biological commandment. An animal must eternally strive to keep itself warm, moist and supplied with oxygen, sugar, protein, salts, vitamins and the like, often within precise limits. Too great a change in its internal economy means death.

The spectacular flying performances of birds—spanning oceans, deserts and whole continents—tend to obscure the more important fact that the ability to fly confers on them a remarkably useful mechanism to preserve their internal stability, or homeostasis. Through flight birds can search out the external conditions and substances they need to keep their internal fires burning clean and steady. A bird's wide search for specific foods and habitats makes sense only when considered in the light of this persistent, urgent need for constancy.

The power of flight opens up to birds an enormous gaseous ocean, the atmosphere, and a means of quick, direct access to almost any spot on earth. They can eat in almost any "restaurant"; they have an almost infinite choice of sites to build their homes. As a result birds are, numerically at least, the most successful vertebrates on earth. They number roughly 25,000 species and subspecies, as compared with 15,000 mammals and 15,000 fishes.

At first glance birds appear to be quite variable. They differ considerably in size, body proportions, color, song and ability to fly. But a deeper look shows that they are far more uniform than, say, mammals. The largest living bird, a 125-pound ostrich, is about 20,000 times heavier than the smallest bird, a hummingbird weighing only one tenth of an ounce. However, the largest mammal, a 200,000-pound blue whale, weighs some 22 million times as much as the smallest mammal, the one-seventh-ounce masked shrew. Mammals, in other words, vary in mass more than a thousand times as much as birds. In body architecture, the comparative uniformity of birds is even more striking. Mammals may be as fat as a walrus or as slim as a weasel, furry as a musk ox or hairless as a desert rat, long as a whale or short as a mole. They may be built to swim, crawl, burrow, run or climb. But the design of nearly all species of birds is tailored to and dictated by one preeminent activity—flying. Their structure, outside and inside, constitutes a solution to the problems imposed by flight. Their uniformity has been thrust on them by the drastic demands that determine the design of any flying machine. Birds simply dare not deviate widely from sound aerodynamic design. Nature liquidates deviationists much more consistently and drastically than does any totalitarian dictator.

Birds were able to become flying machines largely through the evolutionary gifts of feathers, wings, hollow bones, warm-bloodedness, a remarkable system of respiration, a strong, large heart and powerful breast muscles. These adaptations all boil down to the two prime requirements for any flying machine: high power and low weight. Birds have thrown all excess baggage overboard. To keep their weight low and feathers dry they forego the luxury of sweat glands. They have even reduced their reproductive organs to a minimum. The female has only one ovary, and during the nonbreeding season the sex organs of both males and females atrophy. T. H. Bissonette, the well-known investigator of birds and photoperiodicity, found that in starlings the organs weigh 1,500 times as much during the breeding season as during the rest of the year.

As early as 1679 the Italian physicist Giovanni Borelli, in his *De motu animalium*, noted some of the weight-saving features of bird anatomy: "... the body of a Bird is disproportionately lighter than that of man or of any quadruped ... since the bones of birds are porous, hollowed out to extreme thinness like the roots of the feathers, and the shoulder bones, ribs and wing bones are of little substance; the breast and abdomen contain large cavities filled with air; while the feathers and the down are of exceeding lightness."

The skeleton of a pigeon accounts for only 4.4 per cent of its total body weight, whereas in a comparable mammal such as a white rat it amounts to 5.6 per cent. This in spite of the fact that the bird must have larger and stronger breast bones for the muscles powering its wings and larger pelvic bones to support its locomotion on two legs. The ornithologist Robert Cushman Murphy has reported that the skeleton of a frigate bird with a seven-foot wingspread weighed only four ounces, which was less than the weight of its feathers!

Although a bird's skeleton is extremely light, it is also very strong and elastic—necessary characteristics in an air frame subjected to the great and sudden stresses of aerial acrobatics. This combination of lightness and strength depends mainly on the evolution of hollow, thin bones coupled with a considerable fusion of bones which ordinarily are separate in other vertebrates. The bones of a bird's sacrum and hip girdle, for example, are molded together into a thin, tubelike structure—strong but phenomenally light. Its hollow finger bones are fused together, and in large soaring birds some of these bones have internal trusslike supports, very like the struts inside airplane wings. Similar struts sometimes are seen in the hollow larger bones of the wings and legs.

To "trim ship" further, birds have evolved heads which are very light in proportion to the rest of the body. This has been accomplished through the simple device of eliminating teeth and the accompanying heavy jaws and jaw muscles. A pigeon's skull weighs about one sixth as much, proportionately, as that of a rat; its skull represents only one fifth of 1 per cent of its total body weight. In birds the function of the teeth has been taken over largely by the gizzard, located near the bird's center of gravity. The thin, hollow bones of a bird's skull have a remarkably strong reinforced construction. Elliott Coues, the nineteenth-century U. S. ornithologist, referred to the beautifully adapted avian skull as a "poem in bone."

The long, lizard-like tail that birds inherited from their reptilian ancestors has been reduced to a small plate of bone at the end of the vertebrae. The ribs of a bird are elegantly long, flat, thin and jointed; they allow extensive movement for breathing and flying, yet are light and strong. Each rib overlaps its neighbor—an arrangement which gives the kind of resilient strength achieved by a woven splint basket.

Feathers, the bird's most distinctive and remarkable acquisition, are magnificently adapted for fanning the air, for insulation against the weather and for reduction of weight. It has been claimed that for their weight they are stronger than any wing structure devised by man. Their flexibility allows the broad trailing edge of each large wing-feather to bend upward with each downstroke of the wing. This produces the equivalent of pitch in a propeller blade, so that each wing beat provides both lift and forward propulsion. When a bird is landing or taking off, its strong wing beats separate the large primary wing feathers at their tips, thus forming wing-slots which help prevent stalling. It seems remarkable that man took so long to learn some of the fundamentals of airplane design which even the lowliest English sparrow demonstrates to perfection.

Besides all this, feathers cloak birds with an extraordinarily effective insulation—so effective that they can live in parts of the Antarctic too cold for any other animal.

The streamlining of birds of course is the envy of all aircraft designers. The bird's awkwardly angular body is trimmed with a set of large quill, or contour, feathers which shape it to the utmost in sleekness. A bird has no ear lobes sticking out of its head. It commonly retracts its "landing gear" (legs) while in flight. As a result birds are far and away the fastest creatures on our planet. The smoothly streamlined peregrine falcon is reputed to dive on its prey at speeds up to 180 miles per hour. (Some rapid fliers have baffles in their nostrils to protect their lungs and air sacs from excessive air pressures.) Even in the water, birds are among the swiftest of animals: Murphy once timed an Antarctic penguin swimming under water at an estimated speed of about 22 miles per hour.

A basic law of chemistry holds that the velocity of any chemical reaction roughly doubles with each rise of 10 degrees centigrade in temperature. In nature the race often goes to the metabolically swift. And birds have evolved the highest operating temperatures of all animals. Man, with his conservative 98.6 degrees Fahrenheit, is a metabolic slow-poke compared with sparrows (107 degrees) or some thrushes (113 degrees). Birds burn their metabolic candles at both ends, and as a result live short but intense lives. The average wild songbird survives less than two years.

Behind this high temperature in birds lie some interesting circulatory and respiratory refinements. Birds, like mammals, have a four-chambered heart which allows a double circulation, that is, the blood makes a side trip through the lungs for purification before it is circulated through the body again. A bird's heart is large, powerful and rapid beating. In both mammals and birds the heart rate, and the size of the heart in proportion to the total body, increases as the animals get smaller. But the increases seem significantly greater in birds than in mammals. Any man with a weak heart knows that climbing stairs puts a heavy strain on his pumping system. Birds do a lot of "climbing," and their circulatory systems are built for it.

HEART	PERCENT OF BODY WEIGHT	HEART BEATS PER MINUTE
FROG	.57	22
MAN	.42	72
PIGEON	1.71	135
CANARY	1.68	514
HUMMINGBIRD	2.37	615

The blood of birds is not significantly richer in hemoglobin than that of mammals. The pigeon and the mallard have about 15 grams of hemoglobin per 100 cubic centimeters of blood—the same as man. However, the concentration of sugar in their blood averages about twice as high as in mammals. And their blood pressure, as one would expect, also is somewhat higher: in the pigeon it averages 145 millimeters of mercury; in the chicken, 180 millimeters; in the rat, 106 millimeters; in man, 120 millimeters.

In addition to conventional lungs, birds possess an accessory system of five or more pairs of air sacs, connected with the lungs, that ramify widely throughout the body. Branches of these sacs extend into the hollow bones, sometimes even into the small toe bones. The air-sac system not only contributes to the birds' lightness of weight but also supplements the lungs as a supercharger (adding to the efficiency of respiration) and serves as a cooling system for the birds' speedy, hot metabolism. It has been estimated that a flying pigeon uses one fourth of its air intake for breathing and three fourths for cooling.

The lungs of man constitute about 5 per cent of his body volume; the respiratory system of a duck, in contrast, makes up 20 per cent of the body volume (2 per cent lungs and 18 per cent air sacs). The anatomical connections of the lungs and air sacs in birds seem to provide a one-way traffic of air through most of the system, bringing in a constant stream of unmixed fresh air, whereas in the lungs of mammals stale air is mixed inefficiently with the fresh. It seems odd that natural selection has never produced a stale air outlet for animals. The air sacs of birds apparently approach this ideal more closely than any other vertebrate adaptation.

Even in the foods they select to feed their engines birds conserve weight. They burn "high-octane gasoline." Their foods are rich in caloric energy—seeds, fruits, worms, insects, rodents, fish and so on. They eat no low-calorie foods such as leaves or grass; a wood-burning engine has no place in a flying machine. Furthermore, the food birds eat is burned quickly and efficiently. Fruit fed to a young cedar waxwing passes through its digestive tract in an average time of 27 minutes. A thrush that is fed blackberries will excrete the seeds 45 minutes later. Young bluejays take between 55 and 105 minutes to pass food through their bodies. Moreover, birds utilize a greater portion of the food they eat than do mammals. A three-weeks-old stork, eating a pound of food (fish, frogs and other animals), gains about a third of a pound in weight. This 33 per cent utilization of food compares roughly with an average figure of about 10 per cent in a growing mammal.

The breast muscles of a bird are the engine that drives its propellers or wings. In a strong flier, such as the pigeon, these muscles may account for as much as one half the total body weight. On the other hand, some species—e.g., the albatross—fly largely on updrafts of air, as a glider does. In such birds the breast muscles are greatly reduced, and there are well-developed wing tendons and ligaments which enable the bird to hold its wings in the soaring position with little or no effort.

A bird may have strong breast muscles and still be incapable of sustained flight because of an inadequate blood supply to these muscles. This condition is shown in the color of the muscles; that is the explanation of the "white meat" of the chicken and the turkey—their breast muscles have so few blood vessels that they cannot get far off the ground. The dark meat of their legs, on the other hand, indicates a good blood supply and an ability to run a considerable distance without tiring.

After a ruffed grouse has been flushed four times in rapid succession, its breast muscles become so fatigued that it can be picked up by hand. The blood supply is simply inadequate to bring in fuel and carry away waste products fast enough. Xenophon's *Anabasis* relates the capture of bustards in exactly this manner: "But as for the Bustards, anyone can catch them by starting them up quickly; for they fly only a short distance like the partridge and soon tire. And their flesh was very sweet."

In birds the active phase of the breathing cycle is not in inhaling but exhaling. Their wing strokes compress the rib case to expel the air. Thus instead of "running out of breath" birds "fly into breath."

Probably the fastest metabolizing vertebrate on earth is the tiny Allen's hummingbird. While hovering it consumes about 80 cubic centimeters of oxygen per gram of body weight per hour. Even at rest its metabolic rate is more than 50 times as fast as man's. Interestingly enough, the hovering hummingbird uses energy at about the same proportionate rate as a hovering helicopter. This does not mean that man has equaled nature in the efficiency of energy yield from fuel. To hover, the hummingbird requires a great deal more energy, because of the aerodynamic inefficiency of its small wings and its very high loss of energy as dissipated heat. The tiny wings of a hummingbird impose on the bird an almost incredible expenditure of effort. Its breast muscles are estimated to be approximately four times as large, proportionately, as those of a pigeon. This great muscle burden is one price a hummingbird pays for being small.

A more obvious index of the efficiency of birds' fuel consumption is the high mileage of the golden plover. In the fall the plover fattens itself on bayberries in Labrador and then strikes off across the open ocean on a nonstop flight of 2,400 miles to South America. It arrives there weighing some two ounces less than it did on its departure. This is the equivalent of flying a 1,000-pound airplane 20 miles on a pint of gasoline rather than the usual gallon. Man still has far to go to approach such efficiency.

THE NAVIGATION OF BIRDS

by Donald R. Griffin

FEW NATURAL PHENOMENA have so enchanted and puzzled men in all ages as the migrations of birds. The oracles of Homeric Greece and the augurs of the Roman Empire wove the seasonal appearance and disappearance of wild birds into their everyday religion and mythology. After the Romans, for many centuries birds received less sophisticated attention. Nevertheless their annual comings and goings have always intrigued all sorts of men from dilettantes to professional specialists. Perhaps there is a common denominator in the interest displayed by the augurs of ancient Rome and by the Audubon societies of today. No naturalistic conception of the universe seems really complete unless it deals with bird migration, and even in the most mechanistic modern climates of opinion this has been a phenomenon demanding special explanation. The attempted explanation may be a mechanistic one, but even so it is likely to be less mechanical than explanations of other phenomena. This is as true in these days of relativity, radar and mesons as it was in the time of James Clerk Maxwell and Charles Darwin. Bird migration is still something of a mystery even to those who deny the existence of mysteries.

I must disclaim at once any attempt in this article to offer a solution of the mystery, but it does seem worth while to describe the progress that has recently been made toward an understanding of bird migration. During the past century the patient work of ornithologists has furnished a rather adequate description, if not an explanation, of the main features of bird migrations: their extent, the times of departure and arrival, the approximate routes followed by most species, the speed with which a whole population moves from winter to summer range, or vice versa. Repeated observations have established certain interesting facts, such as that some species migrate by night while others travel in the daytime; that in some species the young and old birds travel together, while in others they may migrate by entirely different routes or at different dates. The success of this description intensifies the urge to understand how the long journeys are accomplished. Of all the questions that have been asked about bird migrations, the most baffling and the most critical is the matter of orientation—how do the birds find their way?

To appreciate the dimensions of this problem one must consider the vast distances that birds often travel in their seasonal flights. While some birds are nonmigratory or travel only a few miles, as from a mountaintop to a neighboring valley, others span a major portion of the globe. One typical example is the tiny ruby-throated hummingbird (*Archilochus colubris*). This species, a familiar one in the eastern U. S., has a summer range that extends from lower Canada to the Gulf Coast and a winter range from the Gulf Coast southward to the Isthmus of Panama. While the summer and winter ranges overlap somewhat, as they do with many birds, it is clear that individuals nesting along the Canadian boundary during the summer must migrate many hundreds of miles to reach even the northern edge of the winter range. The hummingbirds' summer and winter ranges are similar to those of many common songbirds, so that migrations of this length are the rule rather than the exception. A more extreme and spectacular case is that of the golden plover (*Pluvialis dominica*), a short bird or wader slightly larger than a robin. Two closely related subspecies of this bird nest in the arctic latitudes of North America and Siberia and migrate to the Southern Hemisphere in winter. In addition to its great length, this migration route presents other features of interest. First, the adults seem to leave the breeding grounds before the young, so that many of the latter must make the entire journey without guidance from other golden plovers that have previously flown the course. Also, the golden plover does not swim on the water's surface, or at least has very seldom been observed to do so; it appears highly probable that the bird's extensive overwater flights, such as those to the Pacific islands or that from Nova Scotia to the Lesser Antilles, are made without stops for food or rest.

These migration routes are merely examples; many more are known to be just as extensive and to involve equally difficult feats of navigation. There are oceanic birds such as albatrosses, boobies, petrels, shearwaters and fulmars, which spend most of their lives at sea but must fly hundreds of miles to islands to lay their eggs and raise their young. The kingfisher or halcyon was believed in Aristotle's time to lay its eggs in a floating nest and to require a calm sea and fine weather for the safety of the eggs—hence the expression "halcyon days." Modern ornithology has found no birds which build nests floating on the open sea, but it has observed very remarkable habits among such birds as the petrels and shearwaters. Although highly adapted to a life at sea, these birds protect their nests from predators by digging burrows to shelter the eggs and young. Some species come ashore to enter these burrows only under cover of darkness. It is difficult even to guess how they find the islands on foggy nights. Petrels nesting on islands in the Bay of Fundy seem to prefer foggy nights, when they are safer from gulls, for their visits to the burrows, but tremendous problems of navigation must be posed by this searching for the nests.

All of these migrating birds must guide their flight by means of some aspect of their environment which is related in a reasonably reliable fashion to the direction of the goal. We must also take as certain, unless we are to fall back on extra-scientific theories, that this environmental cue must be perceived by the birds; it must stimulate some sense organ or receptor cells, for these are the only functional contacts between a bird's nervous system and its outside environment. Our problem, then, is to find the environmental cue, and also to find the sensory mechanism by which this environmental cue is recognized and channeled into the central nervous system, where it can result in the appropriate actions to move the bird in the right direction.

No one has yet succeeded in solving this problem, and all attempts to do so have been impaled on one or both horns of a dilemma: either the proposed environmental cue has seemed altogether too unreliable, or it has been impossible to demonstrate that the birds could perceive it.

On the first horn of this dilemma we find those who try to account for bird navigation in terms of the known sensory mechanisms, which are much the same in all higher vertebrates. Some have suggested that migrants are guided by visual landmarks. But the overwater routes such as those of the golden plover are devoid of topography for hundreds of miles, although some guidance might be obtained from the ocean swells, which tend to be rather constant in direction over any one part of the ocean. Others feel that wind direction may offer a guiding cue, but winds are notoriously changeable, and only if the bird knew the wind direction characteristic of each type of air mass and weather condition along its route could it guide itself from arctic to tropics.

The sun or other celestial points of reference might be guides, but a bird navigating by them would be obliged from hour to hour to change the angle between its flight path and the azimuth of the heavenly body upon which its attention might be fixed. Additional but smaller shifts would be made necessary by changes in longitude and latitude as the migration progressed. An even more obvious objection is that the birds migrate during overcast weather and even on cloudy nights. Answers are possible to these objections, such as the fact that even on heavily overcast days the sun's position is to some extent revealed by the pattern of sky brightness, the sky being slightly brighter in that half containing the sun. Yet it is difficult to be at all satisfied with any of the attempts to find environmental cues which would be adequate as a basis for the navigation of migrants and yet which lie within the sensitivity range of the known sensory mechanisms.

Turning then to the other horn of the dilemma, we find a variety of ingenious theories hung up on formidable objections from the point of view of the sensory physiologist. Best known, perhaps, is the idea that birds have the equivalent of a magnetic compass—that they can perceive the earth's magnetic field in some manner and guide their migrations accordingly. This theory has assumed many forms. Some postulate that birds can tell the direction of magnetic north, while others argue that they can judge the intensity of the earth's field, or the horizontal or vertical components in it. One of the most elaborate theories holds that birds can sense the angle of dip in the lines of force constituting the earth's magnetic field. The numerous but quite unconfirmed reports that birds' navigation is affected by the electromagnetic waves from radio transmitters are usually linked to the theories of magnetic sensitivity, though not in any precise manner.

The tendency of these theories is to postulate that the birds are aware of two effects, one of which informs them of their latitude and the other of their longitude. The migration is conceived of as a movement resulting from some type of simple reaction or "tropism" (automatic orientation) of which even one-celled protozoans are capable. By assuming sufficiently sensitive receptors, one can thus picture the actual reactions of the birds in very simple terms. But these theories must face the fact that no one has shown that birds can sense a magnetic field as weak as the earth's, any more than we can ourselves. Birds have been subjected to very intense magnetic fields in the hope that they would exhibit some response—indicating that they felt the magnetism. But no such response has ever been demonstrated, and we must therefore discard the magnetic theories unless and until such a sensitivity can be shown.

A really new theory was advanced recently, namely that birds orient themselves by means of mechanical forces arising from the earth's rotation. These forces might take many forms, such as 1) an increase in the apparent weight of a flying bird depending on the direction of its flight, 2) a lateral force exerted on fluids flowing through its arteries, or 3) the so-called "Coriolis force," which causes a body traveling with uniform velocity through the air to trace a slightly curved path over the earth's surface, owing to the fact that while the flying object is in the air the earth rotates underneath it. These effects are of a type which might be within the range of a bird's sense organs, since they involve mechanical acceleration for which the bird has specialized receptors in the inner ear labyrinth. But the difficulties in the way of a bird's being able to make quantitative distinctions in such effects are enormous. The variation in weight is only one part in several thousand, and it could easily be masked by the much larger accelerations resulting from flight itself, to say nothing of the slightest turbulence of the air, or even the bird's own breathing and heartbeat. Similarly, the lateral forces on arteries are infinitesimal compared with the effects of turbulence within the blood and the waves of pulse pressure traveling from the heart. Thus this hypothesis seems scarcely more plausible than the magnetic theories.

One reason for our persisting ignorance concerning the sensory basis of bird navigation is the difficulty of making detailed observations of an individual bird while it is actually setting its course. One can watch wild birds leave their breeding grounds; one can observe them passing various points on their way south; one can note the time of arrival and departure of a species in any region; and by observing where the birds are concentrated during migration one can map with fair accuracy the chief routes traveled. But birds can seldom be followed from the ground for more than a mile or two, and such observations disclose birds flying in all directions even during the height of a migration. Thus one can very seldom be sure that at a given moment any particular bird is actually starting a migratory flight in the correct direction. Bird-banding—the fixing of numbered metal bands about the legs of birds—has demonstrated the extent of many individual journeys, but for our purposes this method suffers from several limitations: the percentage of recoveries at significant distances from the point of banding is extremely small, and almost invariably several weeks or months elapse before the birds are recovered at a distance, so that one has little assurance from the results of banding alone that a bird traveled directly from the point of banding to the point of recovery. Nor can one tell anything of the route followed, or the conditions under which the migration was performed, much less the sensory mechanism employed.

Direct experiments with migrating birds are extremely difficult, but some have been performed, notably by William Rowan in Canada and Werner Rüppell in Germany.

Rowan kept young crows in captivity in Alberta until November, when all wild crows had left the area for their winter range 1,000 miles or so to the southeast. Then the young crows were banded and released with a widely publicized reward for their recovery, dead or alive. Several were shot and reported within the next few weeks. All of those that had traveled any distance were recovered within 30 degrees of the normal migration route. This showed that young crows could take the correct direction without adults to guide them.

Rüppell's experiments involved a European species of crow which could be captured in large numbers during spring migration on the Baltic coast of East Prussia. In his most clearcut experiment some 500 crows were captured at Rossitten on the Baltic and released 465 miles to the west at Flensburg, a locality which this population of crows had never visited previously. The normal summer range of these crows, as revealed by the recovery of many birds banded over a period of years, was an area northeast of Rossitten. When the crows displaced to Flensburg were retaken during the following spring and summer, all recoveries came from the area to the northeast of Flensburg; in other words, the crows had shifted their summer range westward. Evidently these crows continued their spring migration in roughly the normal direction even though they were displaced into different territory.

Such experiments with migrating birds are valuable, but they are also very laborious. One still does not know much about the actual routes flown by individual birds, nor is there much opportunity for direct experimentation. Another procedure has therefore been widely used to study bird navigation. It is a sort of artificial migration which can be arranged experimentally in many species by catching adult birds at their nests, while they are incubating eggs or caring for young, and transporting them to a distance before release. Birds treated in this way often return hundreds of miles, behaving somewhat like homing pigeons. These artificial homing experiments, as they are called, bring one a step closer to the direct observation of the individual navigating bird. Here one knows at least the beginning and end points of the journey; by watching the nest, one can observe the bird's return and accurately measure the total elapsed time for the homing flight.

The homing performances of various wild birds in these experiments seem almost as spectacular as their natural migrations. The first experiments of this type were those of John Watson and Karl Lashley with noddy and sooty terns (*Anoüs stolidus* and *Sterna fuscata*) nesting near Key West, Florida. Some of these birds returned even when carried 855 miles northwest to waters where these two species are seldom seen. More recent experiments have involved swallows (*Hirundo rustica*) which returned 1,200 miles from Greece and Spain to nests near Berlin. In another series of experiments, four out of six herring gulls (*Larus argentatus*) nesting on the Massachusetts coast returned from Chicago, 870 miles inland. The most startling case is that of a strictly marine species—the Manx shearwater (*Puffinus puffinus*)—which returned in 14 days from Venice to its nest on an island near Wales. Presumably it flew all the way over water (since shearwaters are almost never seen inland), using a roundabout route of at least 3,700 miles by way of the Mediterranean, the Straits of Gibraltar and the Atlantic.

So striking are these homing performances of wild birds that they have been widely cited as experimental evidence for the theories of special sensory mechanisms—evidence which to many has seemed fully as important as the natural migrations. Thus the magnetic theorists describe the behavior of a homing bird as a return toward the latitude and longitude of the home area by the simple following of gradients in the magnetic sensations. This theory does not appear to be supported by experimental test, however, for when small magnets are attached to a homing bird or when it is exposed to a strong magnetic field its performance does not seem to be affected.

Certain other studies of homing birds have led to an unexpected conclusion: that when released in really strange territory birds are not able to head directly home but explore wide areas, often flying in quite the wrong direction until they reach territory which they have visited before and where they can presumably find familiar landmarks to guide them home. Birds do not return as quickly or in as high percentages from unfamiliar territory as from equally distant areas which they have visited before. Moreover, the average speed of return in homing experiments is far below the birds' known velocities of flight. Even allowing considerable time for resting and feeding along the route, there remains time for wide deviations from the straight line connecting the release point and home. Occasional spectacular cases like that of the shearwater released at Venice would be expected as a result of chance; significantly, a second shearwater carried to Venice did not return until a year later.

To test the hypothesis that birds find their way home by exploration, it was necessary to learn something about the actual routes they flew. By learning to fly light airplanes, Raymond J. Hock and I were able to achieve this objective. We managed to follow a group of gannets (*Morus bassanus*) in the air for a considerable part of their homing flight. Gannets are sea birds, feeding on fish. A large number nest on Bonaventure Island in the Gulf of St. Lawrence. Their large size and white color render them easily visible from the air. Several were transported about 215 miles west southwest from the island and released on fresh water near Caribou, Maine. They were surrounded by completely unknown territory; to reach their nests they had to fly for at least 100 miles over land. Yet they displayed a homing ability quite comparable to that of other wild birds. Those released at Caribou averaged almost 100 miles per day during the return flight. The significant advance over previous homing experiments was our ability to follow the return routes of eight of the seventeen birds released at Caribou for periods as long as nine and a half hours and distances as great as 230 miles. The birds ranged and circled over large areas in clearly exploratory fashion before they "homed" on their island nests.

One naturally asks whether the presence of the airplane did not cause the birds to behave abnormally. The gannets showed no fear of the plane even when it was within 500 feet; at least they did not turn away from their previous course at our approach, as many birds do when an airplane comes near. Nevertheless we kept 1,500 to 2,000 feet above the gannets during these observations in order to minimize the chances of influencing their choice of route. But the best indication that the airplane did not disturb the gannets was that the homing performance of a control group which was not followed was almost exactly the same with respect to average speed and percentage of returns as the performance of the eight birds we observed from the air. If the airplane influenced or frightened the gannets, it did not prevent them from returning to their nests at the normal speed.

These observations seem to confirm several lines of indirect evidence that the homing ability of both wild birds and domestic homing pigeons is based largely on visual landmarks, or on exploration when the birds are released in unfamiliar territory. Such a conclusion leaves us in something of a quandary. The homing experiments argue strongly that birds do not possess any special sensory mechanism that can guide them home or inform them of their latitude and longitude. Yet in the case of natural migrations it is preposterous to suggest that the birds are merely exploring. Even young birds without guidance begin their first migration in roughly the correct direction, as shown by the experiments of Rowan and others. Individual young birds may deviate 20, 30 or even 40 degrees from the average direction for the species, but virtually none go north in the fall.

There remains the possibility that migratory birds can determine the direction appropriate for a particular migration. But this is of no help when they are artificially transported into unknown territory, for then they cannot know whether home lies north, east, south or west. If this be true, then clearly the homing experiment would not reveal the basis of navigation by migrants. For this reason, among others, the best hope for future progress seems to be offered by experiments with actual migrations, particularly if the routes flown by individual birds can be traced as we were able to trace the routes of homing gannets.

The late Werner Rüppell, who was the leading European investigator of these phenomena until his death during the war, originally postulated that the homing of wild birds depended upon a mysterious and unidentified "sense of direction." But in his last paper, describing the experiments with migrating crows which I have cited previously, Rüppell suggested that the position of the sun might be the guiding cue. Such a theory is certainly rendered more plausible by the recent demonstration of the Austrian zoologist Karl von Frisch that bees locate sources of food with reference to the position of the sun in the sky, as is explained in the chapter on "The Language of the Bees" by August Krogh.

These questions cannot be settled without specially devised experiments, which should include prolonged following of individual birds from the air and a close correlation of the birds' behavior with meteorological data. For instance, it would be most valuable to learn whether birds begin a migratory flight in the correct direction under heavily overcast skies when no celestial objects are visible. The fact that birds are observed migrating under such conditions is not conclusive evidence, for the overcast may be a local one and the birds might have started their flight 50 or 100 miles away under clear skies, holding their course in thick weather by means of local cues such as topography or wind direction.

The novelty and the expense of airplane observations of individual birds have prevented such work from being undertaken on any extensive scale, but I hope that the increasing practicability of light airplanes (and eventually helicopters) will serve as a stimulus for such work in the future. Perhaps we can look forward in the next few years to the emergence of a group of air-minded ornithologists who will trace significant portions of the migration routes of individual birds with a simultaneous understanding of the ocean of air in which they move. Such research, wisely conducted and on an adequate scale, might well provide the key to these ancient and baffling questions.

SONAR IN BATS

by Donald R. Griffin

ALMOST EVERYONE has at least a casual acquaintance with bats; those "winged mice" which fly about in the dusk or darkness and occasionally enter the attics of houses. To some they are terrifying creatures alleged to entangle themselves in women's hair. In folklore and artistic symbolism they are manifestations of the supernatural—images of evil spirits in our culture but symbols of good luck in the Chinese. To the naturalist they are bizarre and obscure animals of which more than 1,000 species have been described. In recent years, however, bats have come to be mentioned in a quite different context, often in the same breath with the elaborate developments of modern electronics. Thus I have heard in widely scattered places—in a subway, in a schoolroom, in a bar—the bald statement "bats have radar." This startling idea seems well on its way to become common knowledge, although strictly speaking it is quite untrue. Yet there is no doubt that a bat can fly through the total darkness of a cave, locating and dodging obstacles in its path. Sometimes hundreds of individual bats fly through the same passageways at the same time, all dodging the jutting rocks as well as one another. If they possess neither magic nor radar, how do they do it?

Bats' eyes are not the means by which they guide their flight in the dark. Biologists have known since the late eighteenth century that bats retained their skill even when blinded. Lazaro Spallanzani of Italy was the first man to experiment with the power of bats to avoid obstacles; before 1800 he and Louis Jurine of Switzerland had discovered that if bats' *ears* were covered, they became helpless and collided even with large and conspicuous obstacles. But a bat's flight is silent, or very nearly so; and it was difficult to imagine how the ears could help to locate threads stretched across a room or the branches of trees in a forest. As one critic wrote sarcastically in 1809, "Since bats see with their ears, do they hear with their eyes?" Not until 1920 was a plausible explanation suggested by the English physiologist H. Hartridge, who watched bats flying through darkened rooms and advanced the theory that they might be orienting themselves by means of ultrasonic sounds too high in frequency for human ears to hear.

In 1938 I had the opportunity to bring some live bats to the laboratory of G. W. Pierce of the Harvard University Department of Physics. Pierce had developed an apparatus that detected ultrasonic sounds, and it was at once apparent that the bats made sounds which we could not hear but which were readily detected by the Pierce apparatus. The frequency of the sounds was roughly 50,000 cycles per second, whereas human ears can hear sounds only within a range of about 20 to 20,000 cycles. Young children can hear high frequencies more easily than adults; and smaller mammals such as cats, guinea pigs and rats can hear frequencies up to 30,000 cycles or perhaps even higher. The little brown bats (*Myotis l. lucifugus*) that we used in these experiments are much smaller than house mice, and my colleague Robert Galambos has shown by experiments that the inner ear of these bats is sensitive to frequencies as high as 100,000 cycles. Galambos and I worked together from 1939 to 1941 analyzing in some detail the obstacle-avoidance techniques of bats, and we confirmed Hartridge's theory in every respect.

We tested the skill of the bats by making them fly through a room divided across the middle by a row of wires hanging vertically from the ceiling and spaced a foot apart. The bodies of the bats almost never collided with a wire 3/16 of an inch in diameter, though occasionally their wingtips brushed against the wire in passing. In 90 per cent of the passages the bats did not touch such heavy wires at all. Smaller wires were more difficult for the bats to detect; their score with wires $1/20$ of an inch in diameter was only 70 per cent. With wires three one-thousandths of an inch thick they did no better than chance alone would allow. Stopping the ears or covering the mouth of a bat also reduces its score to the chance level.

Other experiments showed that the bats needed both ears for normal obstacle avoidance. With one ear covered they could detect the walls but avoided wires only a little better than with both ears stopped. Locating the source of a sound requires two ears in men and other animals which have been tested, so it seems natural that a bat would detect the position of an obstacle by localizing the source of the echo in the same way. The reason both ears are required for auditory localization is that sound waves coming from the side reveal their origin by reaching the two ears at different times, at different intensities or in different phase relations. Bats emit their ultrasonic cries in rapid succession as they approach difficult obstacles such as wires, sometimes giving as many as 30 to 50 cries per second. When the obstacles are numerous and complicated the rate of the emission is increased; when the path is clear the rate is lower.

We were surprised to find on close study that the ultrasonic sounds were faintly audible to us; they were always accompanied by a click that could be heard in a quiet room if the bat was held within a few inches of one's ear. When the cries were emitted in rapid succession the clicks fused into a sound best described as a buzz. The bats also gave occasional loud and clearly audible cries, but these were not at all related to obstacle detection and came usually when a bat was struggling to escape from an experimenter's hands. At times bats seem to emit their ultrasonic cries with a louder audible component which can be heard at several feet. These bats are usually in poor physical condition or not completely awakened from the torpor of hibernation; it might be said that they are "not in good voice." During the same wartime years as our experiments, the Dutch zoologist Sven Dijkgraaf also turned his attention to bats while he was living under the hardships of the Nazi occupation. Working alone with no special instruments and without knowing of our studies, Dijkgraaf noticed the relationship between these faintly audible clicks and buzzing sounds and the avoidance of obstacles. Relying on his own ears and careful observation of a few individual bats, he discovered virtually all the facts I have described above. He naturally thought in terms of faint audible clicks, however, rather than ultrasonic sounds. Like so many scientific findings, this elucidation of the bat's method of obstacle avoidance was thus achieved almost simultaneously in widely separated parts of the world.

Since the war I have made more refined measurements of the properties of bats' ultrasonic sounds and have photographed their wave-form as seen on the cathode-ray oscilloscope. These photographs show that a typical ultrasonic cry lasts only for a very short interval of time—about one five-hundredth of a second. An audible sound of this extreme brevity is heard as a sharp click. The cathode-ray oscilloscope also revealed other unsuspected details. Each cry contains about 100 individual waves of sound; but instead of being evenly spaced across the oscilloscope screen, the waves are always crowded together at the beginning of the pulse and farther apart at the end, showing that the frequency drops during its fleeting lifetime. The first few waves may have a frequency of 100,000 cycles or even higher, while at the end of a pulse the frequency may have dropped to 40,000 cycles or even lower. In other words each pulse, though it contains only about 100 waves, is frequency-modulated. The frequency always seems to drop at least an octave from the beginning to the end of the pulse.

To understand what use this frequency modulation may have, let us consider how much space each pulse occupies as it spreads out ahead of the flying bat at the characteristic speed of sound: 1,130 feet per second. It is most convenient to express this velocity of sound in terms of the distance traversed in a thousandth of a second, or one millisecond, since the duration of the bat's pulses is measured in such microscopic intervals of time. In one millisecond sound travels 1.13 feet; and since the duration of the pulse is about two milliseconds the first waves are roughly two feet ahead of the bat's nose when the last waves leave its mouth. If there is a solid object three feet away, the first waves of the echo will return to the bat's ears after about six milliseconds (we may neglect the motion of the bat since it is very slow compared with the velocity of sound). But suppose the object is closer, perhaps only nine or ten inches ahead. Bats often fly this close to an obstacle and then turn aside, and other observations show that they can use their pulses of ultrasonic sound to detect objects as close as six inches. Under these conditions an echo will return to the bat's ears before the pulse can even finish leaving its mouth. Since the emitted pulse must sound far louder to the bat than the echo from a small object, how does the animal distinguish the faint echo from the emitted pulse? I cannot give a positive answer, but it would seem easier for a bat to distinguish between echo and original pulse if the two differed in frequency, as in fact they do. For it is the high-frequency beginning of the echo that overlaps the low-frequency end of the emitted pulse.

Another important consideration is the surprisingly high intensity of these ultrasonic pulses or clicks. A few inches in front of the animal's mouth the intensity, in terms of sound pressure, may be ten times as great as the noise of a subway train passing the station platform. This is about 100 dynes per square centimeter, or 113 decibels on the conventional scale of sound intensity. Sounds as intense as these must be very loud to the bat's ears, yet the bat must be extremely sensitive to these same frequencies in order to pick up the faint echoes from small objects. This problem may be simplified by a mechanism in the middle ear which serves to reduce the sensitivity of the receiving mechanism. This consists of a set of muscles which vary the tension of the ligaments connecting the ossicles of the middle ear, those tiny bones which conduct the mechanical energy of sound waves from the eardrum to the sensitive cochlea where it can stimulate nerve fibers. The contraction of these muscles is known to reduce the sensitivity of the ears of men and experimental animals such as guinea pigs. The muscles presumably have a similar function in the bat, perhaps contracting with the emission of each ultrasonic pulse to protect the delicate ear from the blast of emitted sound. Significantly these muscles are enormously large in bats, considering the small size of the animals. One, the *tensor tympani*, is about the same actual size in a bat as in a cat, which weighs more than 100 times as much. Perhaps these highly developed muscles serve as the protective devices I have suggested; perhaps they do not.

Having considered some of the adaptations of structure and function which enable bats to locate objects at a distance, we can return to the statement "bats have radar." Now we can appreciate both its truth and its error. Sound waves are used rather than radio waves; but there are startling similarities between the bat's method and radar, not only in basic principles but even in some of the less obvious details. An even closer analogy is sonar, the apparatus that locates objects beneath the surface of the ocean by generating sounds which echo from the bottom, from submarines or even from fish. All three devices have much in common. Each employs bursts of energy which are projected outward in order to detect distant objects by means of echoes. In all three systems short wavelengths, i.e., high frequencies, are advantageous because they permit the detection of smaller objects. The principle involved here is the same one that sets a lower limit to the size of objects visible through a microscope by ordinary light, although still smaller objects may be photographed by the shorter waves of ultraviolet radiation. If the object is much shorter than the length of the impinging waves, the waves flow past without appreciable reflection or scattering. The wavelengths employed by the three systems are all roughly the same: 1.5 to 3 centimeters for modern airborne radar systems, 10 centimeters or less for sonar, and about .6 centimeter for the bat's ultrasonic sounds. The bats use the shortest wavelengths of the three, but they are concerned with the smallest obstacles.

Radar and sonar engineers have found it advisable to suppress the sensitivity of the receiving device while the original signal is being emitted; otherwise a receiver sensitive enough to detect the faint echoes would be overloaded and perhaps damaged by the intense emission. As we have seen there is also an effective suppressing mechanism in the bat's ear. A further similarity is that all three systems find it advantageous in many cases to concentrate the emitted energy in two ways. The energy is concentrated in time by employing brief pulses rather than continuous emission, and it is concentrated in direction by focusing it in a beam. Pulsing has the obvious advantage of providing silent periods for listening to echoes, but there is also another merit to pulsed emission. The ease of detection of an echo is determined by the instantaneous intensity, so that a given average power output achieves better results if projected in brief pulses of high intensity rather than in weaker signals of longer duration. Parabolic radar antennae are familiar sights on ships and at our larger airports, and in view of other similarities between bats and radar it was no surprise to find that the bats' ultrasonic pulses are concentrated in the forward direction.

Another phenomenon related to the bat's system of obstacle detection is the use of sound by totally blind people, who are sometimes extraordinarily skillful in finding their way about. Most persons who have been sightless for several years but are otherwise in good health have this ability to some extent, but even those in whom it is best developed may not realize that their skill is based on hearing. Often they may sincerely believe that they feel objects with their foreheads or faces in time to stop before colliding with them. Yet recent experiments have shown that blind people lose most if not all of this ability when their ears are tightly stopped. They seem to have developed a method of orientation resembling the bat's but employing audible sounds. At an Army hospital for the convalescence and rehabilitation of blinded veterans it was found helpful to supply the men with metal plates on the heels of their shoes; the sharp clicks of the metal against floors or sidewalks helped the men avoid obstacles.

Almost everyone has experienced one kind of auditory orientation, namely the differing sounds of footsteps in different rooms. In a large empty room the footsteps are answered by reverberant echoes, and in the dark one can readily tell a room with hard, bare walls from one containing curtains, rugs or other sound-absorbing materials. The forlorn atmosphere of an empty house results partly from the unusually loud echoes from bare walls and floor. It is important in this connection that most auditory orientation by blind people is at such close range that the echoes overlap in time the sounds a person makes in moving about. Partly because of the short distances to important obstacles and partly because the sounds employed have much longer durations than the bat's ultrasonic clicks, the blind have much the same problem as bats which must detect obstacles only a few inches away. In both cases emitted sound and echo may not be heard separately; rather the echo changes the quality of the original sound. In an empty house we hear not temporally distinct echoes but a difference in the quality of our own voices or footsteps. In a similar fashion the bat probably detects obstacles at close range by hearing an altered quality in the sound of its own ultrasonic clicks.

Had biologists understood a few decades earlier the methods by which bats orient themselves, might not the invention of radar and sonar have come sooner? Or might we not already be in a position to perfect acoustic means for self-guidance by the blind? A prominent zoologist has broadcast the mistaken belief that our studies of bats aided the wartime development of radar; actually, our findings were not published until 1940, when radar was already in military use. Yet, granted that in this case the engineers anticipated the biologists, one may speculate whether this sequence is inevitable.

SONAR IN BIRDS

by Donald R. Griffin

IN HIS ACCOUNT of his explorations in South America 155 years ago, the German scientist Alexander von Humboldt described a remarkable cave-dwelling bird he found there. The bird is called the guácharo (Spanish for "one who cries and laments"). Humboldt visited the great Cavern of the Guácharos near the town of Caripe in the highlands of Venezuela.

The guácharo, he reported, was "the size of our chickens," with a wingspread of three and a half feet, and had "the mouth of a goatsucker, the bearing of a vulture . . . an extremely strong beak furnished with a double tooth" and blue eyes which were "dazzled by the daylight." A nocturnal bird, it quit the cave at nightfall to feed on fruit. The bird is covered with extensive deposits of fat, and it was and still is prized for its oil—a transparent, odorless, butter-like food that was said to keep for a year without becoming rancid. (Humboldt named the bird *Steatornis caripensis*—the oil bird of Caripe.) Once a year the Indians went into the cave with long poles, knocked down the guácharo nests from the high roof of the cave and killed several thousand of the nestlings. Then they extracted the oil by melting down the squabs in clay pots over brushwood fires outside the cave.

One of the most remarkable attributes of the guácharo, as Humboldt observed, was the great "volume of its voice." He wrote: "It is difficult to convey any idea of the frightful noise which thousands of these birds produce in the dark portions of the cavern. . . . The sharp and piercing sounds of the guácharos are reflected from the rocky vault, and the echoes reverberate from the depths of the cavern."

This part of Humboldt's account had intrigued me for some time. Here was a bird that flies about in dark caves uttering sharp cries. I had been working on the navigation of bats, as explained in the preceding chapter, and had demonstrated that it depends upon the echoes of the bat's high-pitched cries inaudible to human ears. Did the guácharo guide its flight in the darkness by means of a similar sonar-like system in the audible range? I resolved to find out, and so a year ago I retraced Humboldt's footsteps to the Cavern of the Guácharos in Venezuela.

The trip was made possible by the generosity of William H. Phelps, Jr., the well-known ornithologist of Caracas. We took along a portable tape recorder and the same apparatus that we use to detect and analyze the high-frequency sound of bats. In 1953 we had a much more gentlemanly trip to the cave than that described by Humboldt in 1799. Humboldt and his botanist companion Aimé Bonpland had been obliged to climb through a heavy tropical forest, criss-crossing a raging torrent on the way up. We debarked from an airliner at an airport 50 miles from Caripe. Near Caripe was a pastel-tinted "Hotel El Guácharo." We were driven in an automobile up a gravel road to the very mouth of the cave. There we were greeted by a custodian and a crew of guides eager to lead us through the cavern. Indeed, we were told that electric lights were soon to be installed in the cave to save tourists the inconvenience of carrying flashlights.

The oil birds were still there in considerable numbers, now protected by the government. Our first concern was to determine the degree of darkness in which the birds could fly. We therefore walked deep into the cave, past a twilight zone full of nesting birds to a place where turnings in the passage shut out the daylight. Humboldt had described his penetration into the cave in the following words: "We had had great difficulty in persuading the

Indians to pass beyond the anterior part of the cavern, the only part which they visit annually to gather fat. . . . The natives attached mystical ideas to this cave inhabited by nocturnal birds. They believe that the souls of their ancestors reside at the bottom of the cavern. . . . To go to join the guácharos is to rejoin one's fathers, is to die. . . . We walked in a thick mud to a point where we saw with astonishment the development of a subterranean vegetation. The fruits which the birds carry into the cave to feed their young germinate wherever they fall into the mould which covers the calcareous incrustations. Blanched stalks provided with some rudiments of leaves grew to a height of as much as two feet. . . . These traces of organization in the midst of darkness aroused a lively curiosity in the natives, otherwise so stupid and so difficult to excite. They examined [the blanched shoots] in silent contemplation inspired by a place which they seemed to dread. . . . The missionaries, despite their authority, could not persuade the Indians to penetrate farther into the cavern. As the roof of the cavern became lower, the cries of the guácharos became more piercing. It was necessary to give in to the pusillanimity of our guides and retrace our steps."

We also found ourselves walking through a meadow of white shoots, just as Humboldt had described. About 2,000 feet from the entrance we arrived at a large chamber called *El Barrial*, which Humboldt apparently did not reach. Picking reasonably dry and comfortable rocks to sit down upon, we turned off all our lights and waited for our eyes to adapt to the darkness so that we could tell whether there was any natural light here. I also set up a camera facing the direction of the entrance, with its entire lens mount removed and its Super XX film directly exposed to whatever daylight might possibly penetrate to *El Barrial*.

Over our heads guácharos circled noisily and called back and forth to one another from ledges 75 to 100 feet high. We waited 25 minutes to assure complete dark adaptation of our eyes. I must admit that this wait in the clamorous darkness was an uneasy one, and I am sure more than one finger wandered wishfully toward a flashlight switch. I could only feel the deepest sympathy for the Indians of Humboldt's party and wonder what their reactions would have been if he had ordered them to extinguish their torches and listen to the guácharos in total darkness.

At the end of 25 minutes we were all agreed that no light was to be seen in any direction. Furthermore, the film, which had been exposed for nine minutes, later confirmed this by showing no evidence of light upon development. Our first question was thus conclusively answered: the guácharos did fly in total darkness.

Now we had to determine whether the squawks and shrieks the birds gave forth almost constantly were used for orientation. Bats employ very brief bursts of ultrasonic sound for their echo-locating system. Some of the sounds uttered by the guácharos were rather sharp, short clicks, but these clicks formed only a small part of the sounds we heard during our stay in the cave.

Phelps had noted on a previous visit that the birds made particularly striking noises as they flew out of the cave for their night's hunting. We therefore set up a microphone at the cave entrance. We had to place it on the pinnacle of a rock 15 or 20 feet high, because the birds generally flew near the ceiling some 75 to 100 feet above our heads. Lower down on this rock were arranged amplifiers, a variable electronic filter, a cathode-ray oscillograph, a tape recorder, a 16-millimeter camera to photograph the cathode-ray traces and a storage battery plus vibrator to provide 60-cycle power.

At twilight the guácharos began to fly out. I could scarcely believe these were the same birds we had heard inside the cave that afternoon. For now there were no squawks, clucks or screeches. Instead there came out of the gathering darkness a steady stream of the sharpest imaginable clicks. Each click had a duration of only one to two thousandths of a second—about the same length as the ultrasonic signals of bats. Well into the night the stream of birds and the barrage of clicks continued undiminished. During the whole evening we heard no more than half a dozen of the longer calls and screeches that had predominated inside the cave during the day.

We still lacked any direct evidence that these clicks were actually emitted to locate objects in the birds' path by the echo. Perhaps the clicks were only call notes or symptoms of some other avian emotion the nature of which we could not guess. Accordingly we trapped three birds in a net and took them to an improvised darkroom to make further tests.

The first test was to plug their ears. When both ear canals were tightly stopped with absorbent cotton and cellulose acetate cement, the birds were completely disoriented. In the dark they banged into the walls whenever they took wing. But when the plugs were removed, they were again able to fly about in the dark room without colliding with anything. They also flew without difficulty when the light was turned on even if their ears were plugged.

Even these limited tests were sufficient to show that these birds, like bats, use clicks to avoid obstacles in the dark by echo-location. Unfortunately we were not able to carry the tests much further, and many interesting questions are still unanswered. For example, we do not know how small an object the oil bird can detect. Since the wavelength of its clicks (about five centimeters) is much longer than that of a bat's ultrasonic sounds (less than one centimeter), the guácharo must fail to detect obstacles which a bat could easily locate.

The oil bird's sounds have a frequency of about 7,000 cycles per second—well within the range of human hearing. The question arises: If the oil bird can use such sounds to guide it in the dark, could not a man develop the same skill? The highly perfected human hearing apparatus would appear quite capable of achieving the type of sound analysis necessary for echo-location.

Blind men do indeed achieve a considerable skill in finding their way about, and this ability is often called "facial vision." But the skill is largely lost if the blind man's ears are tightly stopped or if loud noises interfere with the hearing of faint echoes. Very possibly man could develop the echo-locating ability by using short pulses of sound. Since sound travels roughly one foot per millisecond the pulse should be no longer than one or a few milliseconds to return a distinguishable echo at a distance of a few feet. Perhaps properly designed click generators or similar sources of pulsed sound could enhance the ability of blind people to find their way about.

The pragmatic experience of blind men, unconsciously using the taps of a cane, footsteps or other sounds to guide them, may already have produced as much skill in echo-location as the human auditory mechanism allows. But it might not be amiss to see what we can learn from the guácharo and other flying animals which have developed more precise systems of echo-location.

PART 7 INSECTS IN THE LABORATORY

I. METAMORPHOSIS OF INSECTS
by Carroll M. Williams

For the investigation reported here, Carroll M. Williams was awarded the $1000 prize of the American Association for the Advancement of Science in 1950, an award given each year to the best paper presented by a "younger scientist" at the annual meeting. Born in Richmond, Virginia, in 1916, Williams went to Harvard on a coveted Lowell Fellowship after graduation from the University of Richmond. At Harvard, he got an M.A., a Ph.D. and an M.D. and is now professor of biology there.

II. HORMONES IN THE ROACH
by Berta Scharrer

Now Professor of Anatomy at the Albert Einstein College of Medicine, of Yeshiva University, New York, Berta Scharrer received her Ph.D. in zoology from the University of Munich in 1930. She did research on spirochaetic diseases in lower animals at psychiatric and neurological institutes in Munich and Frankfurt-on-Main before coming to America in 1938. Here she has held appointments at the University of Chicago, The Rockefeller Institute for Medical Research, Western Reserve University, and the University of Colorado. Miss Scharrer's principal work today is in the field of invertebrate endocrinology and comparative histology.

III. SPIDER WEBS AND DRUGS
by Peter N. Witt

As a boy in Germany, Peter N. Witt kept some two hundred pets, including an antelope, pigeons, squirrels, turtles and fish and owned a share in the local zoo where he spent Saturday afternoons in and out of the cages watching the animals. He studied medicine in Germany and Austria during the war and worked in field hospitals. Witt is now an experimental pharmacologist at the University of Berne in Switzerland, specializing in comparative studies of the effects of drugs on various species of animals.

METAMORPHOSIS OF INSECTS

by Carroll M. Williams

THE HUMAN INFANT at birth contains about 10 trillion cells—the progeny of a single pair of cells derived from its parents. During the embryonic period of 10 lunar months, many of these cells possess the capacity for unlimited and disorderly growth. From experiments on animals we know that such cells, removed from the early embryo and cultured in a flask of nutrient solution, may grow aimlessly and without apparent restraint. Yet as long as they remain part of the embryo, their behavior is marvelously co-ordinated. As if in conformity to some master blueprint, sooner or later each cell becomes committed to a precise and humble role in the final organism. During the embryonic period each cell also comes under influences that restrict its growth and multiplication; if it did not, the final result would be not an infant but a monster. The original fertilized egg divides into two cells, the two into four, the four into eight, and so on through an average of 43 divisions to produce the 10 trillion cells of the human infant. The process must stop right there. If the cells of the growing embryo underwent 63 divisions, say, instead of 43, the infant at birth would be larger than a sulfur-bottom whale.

So the forces at work in the embryo must do two things: regulate the growth of the cells in the enlarging community and assign to each cell a specific role in the total organism. These forces obviously are not the exclusive property of the higher and more pretentious animals. Even in plants and animals too small to be seen with the naked eye, it is easy to show that the individual parts are held servant to a predictable and hereditary design of the organism as a whole. Evidently the perfection of mechanisms for controlling growth and differentiation was among the earliest accomplishments in the evolution of life.

This being so, biologists have been able to study these mechanisms, so important to the human species, in a varied assortment of "beasts, fowl and creeping things." Indeed, it is fair to say that studies of the human species itself have made scant contribution to our present understanding of the matter; the bulk of our knowledge is based on studies of less intricate organisms ranging from oat seedlings to tadpoles. Particularly illuminating is the investigation of the metamorphosis of insects. Insects that metamorphose are especially interesting subjects for our study because in them the formative processes are prolonged throughout the life span, instead of being restricted to the period of embryonic development, as in most other animals. Insect metamorphosis is an old story to biologists and students of natural history; it has recently been reopened with the fresh purpose of learning what it has to tell us about the basic problems of growth and differentiation.

Consider, for example, an extreme type of metamorphosis, such as that of the fruit fly. The animal's life is partitioned into four distinct stages—egg, larva, pupa and adult. The pertinent events in its metamorphosis actually begin within the unhatched egg. At this stage the eggshell encloses a yolk-filled space of no apparent structure. Under the microscope, however, the yolk particles are found enmeshed in a network of living protoplasm which surrounds a single centrally placed nucleus. It is this nucleus (more precisely, the genes on the chromosomes within the nucleus) that represents the hereditary blueprint of the future organism. In fact there is a double set of blueprints, since the nucleus contains two complete sets of chromosomes and genes, one contributed by the paternal fly and the other by the maternal fly. What we shall witness is the orderly construction of an organism according to a detailed hereditary formula.

The first thing that happens after the egg has been fertilized is a subdivision of the single nucleus into two separate nuclei, followed by a further series of nuclear divisions. There is convincing evidence that each of these divisions is preceded by a duplication of each pair of genes. In consequence the multiplication of nuclei does not dilute the genetic material, although each nucleus is equipped with a full set of genes. The egg at this stage consists of a single yolk-rich cell containing several hundred nuclei. As the latter continue to divide, they seem to be attracted toward the outermost region of the egg. Then for the first time cell boundaries are laid down around the nuclei and the single multinucleated egg is transformed into a hollow, yolk-filled ball of cells.

Only those nuclei that are fortunate enough to land along the axis of the belly of the egg will contribute to the formation of the embryo itself. The vast majority come to rest elsewhere, and are destined to form embryonic membrances that are ultimately discarded. As the English biologist V. B. Wigglesworth has remarked, "the cells are but bricks; whether they play a noble or a humble part in the final building is decided by the chance of where they fall."

Few phenomena in biology are as baffling as the events that now take place: From a region of the ovum that will form the future thorax, there arises an influence of unknown nature that spreads like a wave over the embryo. As it traverses the hollow ball of cells it casts the majority of the cells for the specific parts they will play in the future larval insect. A few hours later the same thoracic center generates a second wave of determination that commits other cells to the formation of specific parts in the pupal and adult insect. Now, though the embryo still consists only of a hollow, yolk-filled ball of cells, the plans of two future organisms, the larval and pupal-adult insects, have already been roughed out. Two living systems exist side by side—one destined to form the larva, the other the pupal and adult fly.

Up to this point any cell in the embryo could have contributed to any part of the final insect, for each cell is equipped with a complete set of genes, and these are the blueprints of the total organism. With one swift stroke the influence of the thoracic center has altered the cells' potentialities. Each cell continues to possess a full set of genes, but these genes now direct the cell toward a specific fate and function. Thus the cell accepts a specialized role in the organism by surrendering its other latent potentialities.

Now the cells committed to the formation of the larva rapidly execute their various developmental tasks. Within a few hours a tiny fly larva crawls from the egg. During the four days that follow, the headless, footless, wingless larva grows rapidly, twice molting its skin. Curiously this growth of the fly larva occurs not by multiplication but solely by enlargement of the cells. When the larva matures it has no more larval cells than were present when it hatched from the egg.

Meanwhile the embryonic cells that were committed to the formation of the pupa and adult also are present, but take no part in the larva's domestic affairs. They are found scattered throughout the larva in the form of little nests of cells called "imaginal disks." These disks are held under biochemical restraint by a hormone circulating in the blood which prevents them from differentiating into the pupal and adult organs. Though the disks grow at approximately the same rate as the larva itself, their growth takes place by cellular division, not by enlargement. In other words, the growing fly larva is a kind of double individual, one within the other and each growing by a totally different method.

When the larva is full grown, its skin hardens and darkens, and the animal rounds into an oval mass. The larva is now motionless and seemingly dead, yet extraordinary events are occurring inside. The larval cells are indeed dying, but simultaneously the imaginal disks throughout the body spurt in growth and differentiate into the organs of the pupal insect. In this process the growing cells utilize the dead larval tissues as a kind of elegant culture medium. The net result is that the larval tissues are replaced by pupal tissues derived from the imaginal disks. Soon afterward the pupal organs are transformed into the complicated structures of the adult fly.

What can be learned from such a peculiar sequence of events? For one thing we see that the fly larva is a rather different organism from the pupa and adult. The imaginal disks, the precursors of the mature animal, live a kind of parasitic existence within the host larva and in the process of pupation appropriate the larval corpse to nourish their growth. Thus the assets of the larva are finally liquidated and reinvested in what may be regarded as a new organism.

From such a life history a further implication is self-evident. There must be some over-all mechanism of control whereby the death of one developmental system, the larva, is synchronized with the birth of a second developmental system, the pupa and adult. This mechanism fortunately has proved more accessible to experimental analysis than the earlier and more perplexing events occurring in the egg. Indeed, some illuminating experiments can be performed with no more equipment than a few dozen insects and a piece of string.

Because of their small size, fly larvae are not as suitable for such experiments as certain larger larvae; for example, the Cecropia silkworm. The experiments consist in tying string around the insect's body in such a way as to divide the animal into two or more horizontal compartments. The most interesting results are obtained when one ligature is placed transversely behind the head and another just behind the thorax, thereby dividing the larva into three compartments—head, thorax and abdomen.

The isolated head promptly dies, but the behavior of the thorax and abdomen depends on the stage of maturity of the silkworm at the time of ligation. If a mature Cecropia silkworm is subdivided before the cocoon is spun, its metamorphosis is completely arrested. Both the thoracic and abdominal compartments continue to live for several months, but neither can transform to the pupal state. This fact suggests that the pupation of the thorax and abdomen requires some factor derived from the head of the caterpillar. And this indeed is found to be the case, for if the same treatment is applied two days later, after the larva has finished spinning its cocoon, the thoracic compartment now undergoes pupation. Evidently during the period of the spinning of the cocoon the head releases the required factor. Further experiments show that the pertinent factor is a hormone which is secreted by about two dozen nerve cells within the brain.

This brain hormone seems to have a limited function. Its principal role is to trigger the secretion of a second hormone by a pair of endocrine organs located in the thorax, the "prothoracic glands." The second hormone in turn acts on the imaginal disks to provoke the transformation of the larva into a pupa. The prothoracic glands secrete this "growth and differentiation hormone" during a period of three days after being acted upon by the brain hormone. If ligatures are placed on the silkworm less than three days after the completion of the cocoon, the thoracic compartment undergoes pupation, but the abdominal compartment does not. Only after the three-day period does the abdomen acquire the necessary concentration of growth and differentiation hormone.

These simple experiments demonstrate that the insect brain is an unusual organ, serving as the highest center in both the nervous and the endocrine systems. A further strange finding is that the growth and differentiation hormone from the prothoracic glands seems to act back on the brain to shut off the secretion of the brain hormone. Thus the endocrinological system of the insect is a kind of self-balancing mechanism, using a biological application of the "negative feedback" principle to regulate the flow of hormone.

The brain and the prothoracic glands control not only the formation of the pupa but the development of the adult moth from the pupa. After the pupation of the Cecropia silkworm, the brain ceases to secrete its hormone for many months. This accounts for the state of dormancy in which the pupa spends the winter. The months of exposure to winter's low temperatures serve to build up the brain's activity again. In the spring the brain releases its hormone and terminates dormancy. Thus does the secretory activity of the brain synchronize the life history of the animal with the seasons.

Although our information is still incomplete, it seems probable that the growth and recurrent molting of insects in the larval stage also require this very same growth and differentiation hormone. There is one important difference, however. During the period of larval life the tissues are exposed to a third hormone secreted by a tiny pair of glands located just behind the brain—the "corpora allata." If these glands are surgically removed when the caterpillars are young and immature, the animals undergo precocious pupation at the very next molt and ultimately develop into midget-sized adult moths.

It appears that this "juvenile hormone" secreted by the corpora allata acts as a stabilizing factor during the larval life of the insect. It does not interfere with the growth of the imaginal disks or of the larva; it merely prevents them from proceeding further in their differentiation. Late in larval life the corpora allata apparently are shut off by some unknown mechanism and discontinue the secretion of juvenile hormone. The imaginal disks, released from this biochemical restraint, immediately respond to the growth and differentiation hormone by differentiating into the pupal parts. And for the larval tissues the same transition signals biological death. In short, the stirring events that culminate in the fabrication of the pupa and the simultaneous death of the larval tissues are set in motion by the production of one hormone and the withdrawal of another.

Surveying our present knowledge of metamorphosis, it is difficult to avoid the conclusion that the post-embryonic development of an insect is the acting out of a sequence of roles which has been assigned the individual cells according to a genetic formula during early embryonic development. Presumably as a result of the mysterious "waves of determination" that sweep over the embryo at that time, each cell is endowed with a detailed program of differentiation, to the execution of which certain specialized tissues such as the brain, prothoracic glands and corpora allata provide specific biochemical cues. Though much has been learned about the latter processes, we cannot yet pretend to understand the earlier mechanisms whereby the cells are made servant to the distant goals of the organism as a whole. For though each cell, as we have seen, is equipped with a blueprint of the total organism, its fate is decided by influences that are the common property of the entire growing system.

Between the gene and the final organism as a unified going concern there is obviously room enough for the labors of a whole generation of biologists. Meanwhile we have cause to rejoice in the proof that the living organism knows what it is doing—and does it effectively.

HORMONES IN THE ROACH

by Berta Scharrer

THE LABORATORY INVESTIGATOR who keeps up a battle to rid his rat colony of cockroaches may well consider giving up the rats and working with the cockroaches instead. From many points of view the roach is practically made to order as a laboratory subject. Here is an animal of frugal habits, tenacious of life, eager to live in the laboratory and very modest in its space requirements. The roach, to be sure, is an awkwardly small animal to work on, but there are varieties of roaches large enough for experiments. A particularly useful subject is a species named *Leucophaea maderae*, and known as the madeira roach. This giant among roaches, nearly two inches long, is a native of Africa and is also found in South America. Our stock colony is derived from specimens which originally arrived in the United States from South America as stowaways in a shipment of laboratory monkeys. The madeira roach was such a stranger here that entomologists at first had difficulty identifying it. The insect quickly made itself at home in the laboratory, however, and we soon saw its possibilities as an experimental animal.

The madeira roach thrives on an inexpensive diet of apples, carrots and dog-chow, and it needs no water other than that in its food. It breeds readily in the laboratory, producing a hatch of 30 to 35 young every three months, and it is unusually long-lived as insects go, with a life expectancy of up to two and a half years. The creature is ovoviviparous: that is, the young hatch from the egg at the moment they leave the mother. Like all insects, the young roaches (nymphs) grow in spurts; they have an average of eight molting periods, with a noticeable increase in size after each molt. Since roaches belong to the relatively primitive class of insects that do not pass through a complete metamorphosis into an adult form (as butterflies and moths do), they have no pupal stage; they merely acquire a pair of wings after the last molt which they do not use for flying.

The tough little creature survives all manner of experimental treatments. It is an ideal subject for surgery, for it needs no anesthetic (it keeps perfectly quiet if fastened between sheets of soft tissue paper) and it is resistant to infection, so the operating instruments need not be sterilized.

Experimental studies of roaches can tell us a great deal more about higher animals than one might suppose. On close inspection the organs of an insect reveal themselves to be basically much like those of higher animals. This should not be too surprising, since all animals have certain basic functions in common, such as the digestion of food and responses to stimuli. The digestive organs of the madeira roach, like those of higher animals, are divided into segments, each of which performs a special task. Food is stored in the foregut and digested in the midgut, the insect's stomach. The roach has salivary glands which secrete a clear fluid. It has a nervous system that controls the proper functioning of these organs. Behind the roach's brain is a small but complex glandular structure consisting of two parts, called the corpora cardiaca and the corpora allata. These tiny organs, less than a tenth of an inch long, are very important to the insect, as we shall see.

Here, then, is an animal in which we can conveniently investigate the factors that control some basic bodily functions common to all animals, such as digestion of food, growth and development. We can have an almost unlimited number of subjects to experiment on and can perform an almost limitless variety of experiments. So far most of the work on the roach has been concerned with its hormonal and nervous systems.

Insects, like man and other vertebrates, have hormones which correlate the activities of the various organs of the body. An insect's development to maturity is controlled by the interaction of two substances—the growth and differentiation hormone and the juvenile hormone. The first is responsible for the insect's molts, its growth in size and the changes that produce its wings and other adult characteristics. The second acts as a checkrein on the first; it holds back any metamorphosis of the insect until the animal has reached the proper size.

There is a simple way to find out the role of each hormone: just remove the gland that produces it. In the madeira roach, though the glands are very small, we can do this without too much difficulty with the aid of a powerful dissecting microscope. Let us see what happens when we remove the corpora allata, one of the hormone-secreting glands in the insect's head. We dissect out the corpora allata from some roach nymphs and watch their development. The immature insects molt, sprout wings and become adults. But they are stunted adults; they look in every respect as if they did not quite make the grade. They are smaller than normal; their wings do not cover the entire body as they should; they are precocious creatures which give every sign of having become adults prematurely. And so they have, for the removal of the corpora allata deprived them of the restraining influence of the juvenile hormone, so that the metamorphosis came before they had reached their full growth.

The corpora allata also play a role in adult madeira roaches, though it is quite different from the function they perform in nymphs. This role has to do with the production of young. The mother roach, we have noted, has a gestation period of three months. Removal of the corpora allata from a mother during the first week of this period prevents her eggs from developing. The yolk destined to nourish the embryo fails to appear, and certain accessory glands that are supposed to furnish a substance needed by the embryo do not function properly. But the corpora allata are important only during the first week or ten days; once the embryos are well started, the gland can be removed without harm to them.

Let us now consider the organ which is closely associated with the corpora allata—the corpora cardiaca. Like the corpora allata, the corpora cardiaca have long been suspected of producing hormones. When we remove this organ from insects, however, we get a disappointing and mystifying result: the insects seem to get along all right without it. What could be the function of the corpora cardiaca? An examination of the head glands of the madeira roach under the microscope offered a clue. The corpora cardiaca are intimately associated with certain peculiar cells that occur in the brain. These cells, called neurosecretory, are both nerve cells and gland cells; they are known to secrete hormones. The corpora cardiaca of the roach contain glandular material of the same kind as the neurosecretory cells of the brain. Apparently this material "migrates" along a nervous pathway from the neurosecretory part of the brain to the adjacent corpora cardiaca, where it seems to be stored in considerable quantity. It looks, therefore, as if the corpora cardiaca serve as a storehouse for the brain-cell hormones.

This interpretation clears up several otherwise puzzling questions. For one thing, it explains why removal of the corpora cardiaca produces no drastic changes; the insects can get along without the reservoir of hormones because they continue to receive a supply of the same hormones from the source in the brain. So far as can be determined, the corpora cardiaca hormones perform exactly the same tasks as the brain hormones; i.e., they control an insect's development, its color adaptation and the maturation of its eggs. What makes the reservoir hypothesis particularly attractive is that it matches a very similar situation in higher vertebrates. For many years it was thought that the posterior lobe of the pituitary gland in man and other mammals secreted its own hormones. But investigators have been puzzled by the fact that these hormones are indistinguishable from hormones secreted by the brain. There is now good evidence that the hormones in the pituitary's posterior lobe are only stored there and actually come from the neurosecretory portion of the brain, by a nervous route such as that taken by the brain hormones in insects. This new turn in our knowledge of the origin and transport of hormones opens up many promising avenues for further research. We are quite aware that the theory still requires more proof, but it serves to show how fruitful the investigation of insects can be, as far removed from mammals as they are.

The madeira roach has made another very significant contribution to our knowledge, this one having to do with cancer. As so often in research work, it all started as an accidental observation. We found that when both the corpora allata and the corpora cardiaca were removed, the roaches often developed tumors in distant parts of the body. The part attacked most frequently was the stomach, but tumors also arose in the forward part of the gut and in the salivary glands. Many of the tumors gave all the signs of malignant cancer: they grew with great speed, invaded healthy tissues and as a rule led to the death of the animal.

We assumed at first that the cause of these pathological growths was a hormonal imbalance, resulting from the removal of the secreting glands. It is well known that interference with the balance of hormones in mammals can produce tumors. But we soon discovered that hormone deficiency was not responsible for the roaches' tumors; they developed such growths even when they were supplied with hormones by grafts of tissue to replace the removed corpora allata. Apparently it was the surgery itself—some accidental injury connected with the removal of the gland—that caused the insects to develop tumors.

On investigation the injury responsible for the tumors turned out, quite unexpectedly, to be the cutting of a nerve. The nerve in question, called the recurrent nerve, is so intimately connected with the head glands of the madeira roach that it is impossible to remove them without cutting it. That the insects' tumors were due to the severing of this nerve was proved beyond question; when the recurrent nerve is cut with fine scissors without injury to the head glands, about 75 per cent of the roaches so operated on develop tumorous growths. Moreover, the tumors grow only in organs controlled by the recurrent nerve.

The reason this finding was so unexpected is that it was the first time tumors had been induced in an animal by an injury to the nervous system. Radiations, hormones, chemicals of various kinds—all these have been proved to produce cancers in experimental animals, but never before have the nerves been clearly and directly implicated, although nervous disturbances have been suspected to contribute to tumors in connection with other factors. The madeira roach experiments now invite further inquiry into possible nervous factors in cancers of higher animals.

A follow-up study of the tumors in roaches has already yielded some interesting results. For example, female roaches are more vulnerable to tumors (i.e., die sooner) than males. But when the sex organs of males and females are removed, the difference in survival rates disappears. This suggests that the roach has sex hormones. Whether or not such hormones are present in any insect has long been a debated question; the madeira roach offers a start toward settling it.

There may well be other fields in which the madeira roach could prove valuable as a tool for experimentation. It may join the fruit fly, the silkworm, the flour beetle and other laboratory favorites from the insect world as a subject for studies in genetics, endocrinology and biochemistry. Dogs, guinea pigs and rats, valuable as they are, do not tell the whole story of animal biology, and the insects can contribute in their own ways to filling gaps in the story.

SPIDER WEBS AND DRUGS

by Peter N. Witt

THE MEMBERS of the zoology department were dead tired. For days they had been trying to make a motion picture film of a spider building its web. Night after night they had waited up in the laboratory to catch their subject in its intricate construction job, but the perverse little creature had refused to perform for their cameras. Each morning they had fallen asleep with exhaustion, only to find on awakening an hour or two later that the spider had spun a beautiful web during their sleep.

In desperation a delegation of the zoologists finally came to my pharmacology department (we were all colleagues at the ancient University of Tübingen in Germany). Could I supply them with a drug which would stimulate the dilatory spider to spin its web when they wanted it to? As it happened, the zoologists found me in a mood of despair that matched their own. I had been experimenting with various drugs to try to find out whether they differed in their effects on human beings. My test drugs (marihuana, mescaline, morphine, scopolamine, Benzedrine) had evoked wonderful responses in my subjects—fantastic dreams, weird visions in color, laughter, tears and all sorts of emotions. But the experiments had failed to yield any answer to my question about specific differences among the drugs.

Naturally I pointed out to the zoologists that I had not the slightest idea how the drugs would affect spiders. Nevertheless I gave them samples of several drugs to try. The next morning my zoology friends returned with news which, though rather disappointing to them, was highly exciting to me: The drug they had administered to the spider had not accelerated its performance, but it had caused the animal to spin a web of a strange shape never seen before.

I at once decided to transfer my experiments from human beings to spiders. Human subjects are moody, complicated, variable and apt to carry over memories from one experiment to the next. Spiders promised to be much simpler subjects for testing the effects of drugs on the central nervous system. Furthermore, they might yield information which could be put to practical use. If spiders responded differently to different drugs, they would afford an easy test for identifying a small amount of an unknown drug—for instance, in cases of accidental or deliberate poisoning.

Fortunately Professor Hans M. Peters and his colleagues in the zoology department had given much study to the web-building of spiders, including the web's geometric shapes, and we joined efforts in what was to prove a fruitful collaboration.

To begin at the beginning, let us see why and how a spider builds its web. The spider we selected for our experiments is *Zilla x-notata*, which spins an orb web. To a spider the sense of touch is what the sense of sight is to man—its most important means of livelihood. Its web, of course, is its tool for catching food. The Zilla spider sits just off a corner of this structure with two forelegs resting on a "signal" thread running from the outer edge to the center of the web. The whole web can be looked upon as a projection of its legs, waiting tensely to communicate any vibration to the spider. The moment a fly's vibrating wings touch the threads of the web, the spider pounces on it, paralyzes it with its poisonous bite and binds it with a sticky thread. Then it proceeds at leisure to suck the juices from its prey.

That touch rather than sight guides the spider was proved by an English amateur scientist who discovered that a tuning fork vibrating with the same frequency as a fly's wings also provokes the spider's assault; so will a vibrating dummy of a fly. On the other hand, if the signal thread is cut so that the spider cannot feel vibrations of the web, it will pay no attention to a fly crossing the web directly in front of it.

If its web is destroyed day after day, the spider will build a new web every day. Normally it spins each web in the same way and in the same pattern. It usually chooses a window or some other frame as the support. First it attaches an end of thread, which it secretes from its thread-forming gland, to one point on the frame; then it may move horizontally along the frame, paying out more thread and dragging it behind, until it has reached a second point a suitable distance from the first. There it pulls the thread tight and fastens the end at the second point. Now it moves back along this "bridge" and spins a new thread perpendicularly from the middle of it, forming a T. Dangling by this thread, the spider steadily extends it by spinning more length until it reaches a fastening point. This completes the first stage of the web construction. The first stage may take any of several other forms, depending on the shape and nature of the site. But the following stages are always the same. The spider proceeds to spin radial spokes from the center to the outer framework of its web. If it has started with the T described above, it climbs back up the vertical member and along the arm of the T to its starting point, all the time letting out new thread. There it pulls the new thread tight across the diagonal of the triangle. This forms a radial member of its web. In like manner the spider goes on spinning new bridges and radii until it has completed a peripheral frame connected to the center by many radial threads. The angle between these radii is remarkably uniform; most of the spacings do not vary by more than one or two degrees. However, the Zilla spider leaves extra space around one spoke which will serve as the signal thread.

Now the spider proceeds to build the cross members that connect the spokes. It does this by spinning a thread which starts near the outer frame and spirals in toward the center (after it has first laid a temporary thread across the spokes to hold them in position while it moves over them). For this so-called "catching spiral" the spider spins an especially delicate thread covered with a thin layer of sticky fluid. Zilla draws the spiral thread from spoke to spoke around the web until it reaches the one next to the signal thread; then it turns and goes back the other way, thus leaving a free sector around the signal thread. As it fills in its web, the spider measures the distance from thread to thread with its legs and probes the tension of the lines to make sure there will be no loopholes through which a fly may escape.

There are some mystifying features about the spider's construction of its spiral. For instance, one would suppose that for the sake of efficiency the animal would begin by spacing the turns of the spiral close together near the periphery, where the radii are far apart, and would widen the interval between the turns as it moved toward the center. But the spider does exactly the opposite: it narrows the spaces between the spiral turns as it approaches the center. Possibly the reason for this strange behavior is a disposition to minimize the distance it must climb from spoke to spoke; however, there seem to be a great many factors involved in the spider's construction of its spiral, and we have only begun to find them out. As will be seen, it is mainly in the spinning of the spiral that spiders show the effects of drugs.

We know that every species of spider makes its own kind of web, and that it builds its characteristic kind by instinct; when a baby spider spins its first web, even if it has never seen a web before it makes one just like its forebears', except on a smaller scale. The drive to build a web is in direct proportion to the spider's hunger. A hungry spider will spend enormous amounts of energy building webs day after day. In our experiments we keep the animals on a diet which is sufficient to keep them healthy and reasonably satisfied with their captivity but is spare enough to make them build a web every night. We use female spiders, because males, being only half the size of females and requiring less food, build webs much less often.

We chose Zilla as the test animal partly because this spider lives outside its web. It will adopt a paper bag as its home and thus is easy to keep captive. To capture a Zilla spider I bait it out of its hiding place in the garden or a window by touching its web with a tuning fork. While it is attacking the fork, I lay a paper bag on the signal thread. When the disappointed spider returns from its fruitless sally, it enters my paper bag without even noticing that its house has been changed. I can fasten the bag to the corner of a portable wooden frame, and thereafter the spider will build web after web on the frame, always returning to the bag as its home. A large array of such frames hangs in front of the enormous window of my laboratory. Each contains a spider.

A spider's web, needless to say, is no easy thing to study. The threads are so thin and delicate that they can hardly be seen, and they break at the slightest touch of a clumsy human finger. Nor will a web keep for any length of time. Because the gossamer threads are difficult to photograph, even with the best modern camera, H. Homann in Germany conceived the excellent idea of thickening the threads by dusting them with a material that does not bother spiders. A glass bowl filled with a solution of ammonia gas in water and another bowl with a solution of hydrochloric acid are placed under the web. The rising vapors from the bowls combine in the air to form fine crystals of ammonium chloride. In 20 minutes the crystals have covered all the threads with a fine white layer, so light that it does not make the delicate filaments sag but thick enough to make every thread stand out clearly when the white-coated web is photographed against a black background with light from the side.

It is important to see every part of the web, for the changes induced by the drug experiments are subtle. The delicate pattern of the finished web is the result of a precise and complicated pattern of movements by the spider. When a spider's central nervous system is drugged, it departs from this pattern, as a man intoxicated by alcohol weaves an erratic course down the street. The spider's errant movements leave their telltale tracks in a distorted web. And we were delighted to discover that each drug always produced its own distinctive aberrations in the spider.

To administer drugs to spiders without alarming them took a little doing. After many experiments, one of our medical students, Dieter Wolff, found a convenient way. A fluid containing the drug, sweetened with sugar to conceal the drug's taste, is injected into the hind part of a fly, where the spider is accustomed to tap the juices. The fly is cut in half, but the spider is lured to it by a tuning fork simulating the vibrations of its wings. Spiders apparently find the taste of the sugar delicious, for they have taken every drug offered in this way.

When we began to test the effects of drugs, one of the first things we noticed was that a spider made drowsy by a sleeping drug would skip the spinning of the longest and most difficult radial threads—those to the corners of the frame. This left conspicuous gaps in its web.

Of the many other effects, most of which we cannot yet even begin to interpret, I shall mention three which seem especially significant. Benzedrine causes the Zilla spider to spin a spiral which has the usual over-all shape but tends to zigzag like an unsteady walker. We strongly suspect that under the influence of Benzedrine the spider loses its ability to locate precisely the points at which it should fix its spiral. Marihuana, in contrast, produces no disturbance of the sense of direction, but it does cause the spider to omit the first part of the spiral: the animal starts closer to the center and leaves the outer part of the web uncovered by cross members. This effect is peculiar to marihuana—it is always produced by that drug, and only by that drug, as far as I know.

The third drug of special interest is scopolamine, which in human beings produces hallucinations and strange disorientations. Scopolamine destroys a spider's sense of direction almost completely. Its spiral no longer takes regular turns around the center but may go off in false directions.

How far can the effects on spiders be compared to effects of the same substances on human beings? This question will never be answered fully, as we cannot interview a spider to find out what it feels and experiences. We can only compare superficially some of the known facts. It is likely that a general disturbance of the functions of the brain shows its effect in distortion of the sensitivity of touch in the spider, as it distorts vision in man. The strange and colorful visual hallucinations that a man experiences under mescaline may take the shape of haptic (touch) hallucinations in the spider. Yet the general course of an intoxication may be alike in both; for instance, the effect may come and go in waves. This is the way scopolamine affects man, and such a rhythm may be responsible for the fact that a spider under the same influence periodically loses and regains the correct direction in building a spiral. But these are mere speculations.

Why should we work with that strange animal, the spider, instead of some familiar higher animal more like man? The answer is that we cannot interview higher animals about their experiences any more than we can spiders, but the little spider gives us every day in its web an objective and measurable report on the state of its health and its nerves. When we have learned how to interpret it, we shall be able to read a most interesting story in that precise and complicated structure.

[illegible]

The third drug of special interest [illegible], which [illegible] than [illegible] produces hallucinations and [illegible] [illegible] and [illegible] of [illegible]. [illegible] [illegible] takes [illegible] [illegible] [illegible].

[illegible] has been [illegible] the same [illegible] on human beings. This question [illegible] [illegible] [illegible] [illegible] [illegible] [illegible] [illegible] [illegible] [illegible] [illegible] [illegible] the general [illegible] of [illegible] [illegible] [illegible] [illegible] [illegible] [illegible] hallucinations [illegible] [illegible] of [illegible] [illegible] [illegible] [illegible] [illegible] [illegible] [illegible] [illegible] the same [illegible] [illegible] [illegible] [illegible].

[illegible] the [illegible].

PART 8 THE PROPER STUDY OF MANKIND

I. CONDITIONING AND THE EMOTIONS
by Howard S. Liddell

From the University of Michigan where he majored in psychology, Howard S. Liddell went to Cornell in 1918 to get a Ph.D. in physiology. The research which he reports here was begun in 1921. For background on his application of classical conditioning procedures, he visited Pavlov's laboratories at Leningrad. Liddell is professor of psychobiology and director of the Behavior Farm Laboratory which is organized around his work at Cornell University.

II. CURIOSITY IN MONKEYS
by Robert A. Butler

Born in 1924, Robert A. Butler is a research psychologist at the Audiology and Speech Correction Center of the Walter Reed Army Hospital. He took up the study of psychology after the last war, receiving his Ph.D. from the University of Chicago in 1951. Before going to his present position he taught at the University of Wisconsin, where he began his work on curiosity in the Primate Laboratory.

III. THE YERKES LABORATORIES
by George W. Gray

An exception among the authors of this book, George W. Gray is a journalist, not a scientist. His post on the staff of the Rockefeller Foundation takes him to universities, observatories and other research institutions throughout the Western Hemisphere looking into and writing reports on work supported by Rockefeller grants. Most of this reporting is addressed to the private audience of the Foundation's directorate, whose lay members appreciate his capacity for reliable and clear reporting as much as other readers. Born in Texas, Gray was educated at the University of Texas and Harvard College and worked for the Houston *Post* and New York *World.* He began specializing in science journalism in the early 1920s, has written a number of books as well as many magazine articles. He is the most frequent contributor to SCIENTIFIC AMERICAN; his "Great Ravelled Knot," which appeared in the October 1948 issue, won the American Association for the Advancement of Science-George Westinghouse $1,000 award for the best magazine article of the year.

CONDITIONING AND THE EMOTIONS

by Howard S. Liddell

THE PRIMITIVE FORCES of man's emotions are more dangerous and more devastating than nuclear fission. Who can doubt that the central scientific problem of our time is the problem of emotion? Thirty years ago the Russian physiologist Ivan P. Pavlov wrote: "Let the mind rise from victory to victory over surrounding nature, let it conquer for human life and activity not only the surface of the earth but all that lies between the depth of the seas and the outer limits of the atmosphere, let it command for its service prodigious energy to flow from one part of the universe to the other, let it annihilate space for the transference of its thoughts—yet the same human creature, led by dark powers to wars and revolutions and their horrors, produces for itself incalculable material losses and inexpressible pain and reverts to bestial conditions. Only science, exact science about human nature itself, and the most sincere approach to it by the aid of the omnipotent scientific method, will deliver man from his present gloom, and will purge him from his contemporary shame in the sphere of interhuman relations."

Sigmund Freud, the founder of psychoanalysis and a contemporary of Pavlov, characterized the emotional dilemma of man in another way:

"Goaded by the id, hemmed in by the superego, and rebuffed by reality, the ego struggles to cope with its economic task of reducing the forces and influences which work in it and upon it to some kind of harmony; and we may well understand how it is that we so often cannot repress the cry: 'Life is not easy.' When the ego is forced to acknowledge its weakness, it breaks out into anxiety: reality anxiety in the face of the external world, normal anxiety in the face of the superego, and neurotic anxiety in the face of the strength of the passions in the id."

The labors of these two geniuses, Freud and Pavlov, laid the foundations for scientific study of the mechanisms and laws of human nature. Freud's method of psychoanalysis and Pavlov's method of the conditioned reflex have revolutionized our conceptions of human behavior and should make possible the scientific management of emotion.

For many years we at Cornell University have been using modifications of Pavlov's conditioned reflex method to study emotional behavior in the sheep and the goat. This attack upon the problem of human emotions may appear a descent from the sublime to the ridiculous, but such an approach was eloquently defended by the great nineteenth-century French physiologist Claude Bernard. In his *Introduction to the Study of Experimental Medicine* he wrote:

"In scientific investigation, minutiae of method are of the highest importance. The happy choice of an animal, an instrument constructed in some special way, one reagent used instead of another, may often suffice to solve the most abstract and lofty questions. In a word, the greatest scientific truths are rooted in details of experimental investigation which form, as it were, the soil in which these truths develop.

"One must be brought up in laboratories and live in them to appreciate the full importance of all the details of procedure in investigation which are so often neglected or despised by the false men of science calling themselves generalizers. Yet we shall reach really fruitful and luminous generalizations about vital phenomena only insofar as we ourselves experiment and, in hospitals, amphitheaters or laboratories, stir the fetid or throbbing ground of life. . . . If a comparison were required to express my idea of the science of life, I should say that it is a superb and dazzlingly lighted hall which may be reached only by passing through a long and ghastly kitchen."

Pavlov lived in his laboratory for more than forty years with his own happy choice of an experimental animal—the dog, "this friendly and faithful representative of the animal world." His notion of the conditioned reflex developed gradually from that association and study. Our own choice of the sheep and the goat to work with has also been happy; they have proved to be admirable animals for our purposes.

To start our story it is necessary to understand precisely what Pavlov meant by the conditioned reflex. Pavlov conditioned a dog to respond to the sound of a metronome in exactly the same way as it responded to the presence of food, i.e., with the same movements and the same salivary and other digestive secretions. He did this by repeatedly sounding the metronome just before the dog took food in its mouth.

This brings out the two ideas essential for an understanding of conditioning and emotional behavior. The first is the *coincidence* of two forced, stereotyped reactions, and the second is the act of *coupling* these basically emotional behaviors. In Pavlov's example the clicking of the metronome elicited a prompt questioning reaction. This primitive sentinel response is itself an unconditioned reflex, like the hungry dog's greedy gulping of the food when it appears. Pavlov called it the "What-is-it?" reflex. He said: "If the animal were not provided with such a reflex, its life would hang at every moment by a thread."

When the metronome and food become coupled, the clicking of the metronome arouses the dog's passionate longing for food and becomes emotionally equivalent to the food itself. If instead of offering food an experimenter squirts a few drops of bitters into a dog's mouth, the animal vigorously shakes its head and secretes an abundance of watery saliva to rinse from its mouth this irritating and disagreeable substance. It can be conditioned then to respond with the same emotionally charged reaction to the sound of the metronome. As a burned child fears the flame, the coincidence of the metronome and bitters in the mouth imparts to the clicking of the metronome the emotional coloring of fear.

Pavlov observed that dogs subjected to too difficult or prolonged conditioning developed chronic emotional disturbances. He called these states "experimental neuroses." When a dog was confused about whether a signal (metronome, tone or light) meant food or no food, it became seriously worried or anxious and this sometimes led to the equivalent of what we ordinarily call a nervous breakdown. This seemingly innocuous and physically harmless procedure became, in Pavlov's laboratory, a standardized maneuver for precipitating at will in any dog a chronic and incapacitating emotional illness. As a consequence of these observations Pavlov's interest in his later years shifted to the problems of psychiatry. He came to believe that the tried and true method of the conditioned reflex could contribute to the solution of these medical problems.

Our own study of conditioning and emotional behavior began thirty-two years ago and has continued without interruption ever since. The study came about in this way. Sutherland Simpson, then professor of physiology in the Ithaca division of the Cornell University Medical College, had for ten years been exploring the problems of thyroid disorder. He was investigating the effects of removal of the thyroid gland upon growth, development and bodily functions. He had selected as the experimental animals the sheep and goat, for several good reasons. In the first place, these animals commonly give birth to twins of the same sex. Thus he could remove the thyroid from one kid of a pair and use the other as a control. Moreover, we suspect that these animals appealed to Simpson's Scottish frugality. They were relatively inexpensive to maintain, they attained conveniently good size, and much was known about their genetics, nutrition, diseases and so on. Finally, when the thyroidless "cretin" sheep died, the wool and mutton of its healthy twin helped defray the cost of the experiment!

Our entrance into the study came in the spring of 1921 when Simpson decided that the new lambs should have their intelligence tested. He reasoned that lambs deprived of their thyroid glands should show a blunted mentality, as human cretins did. But how might one test the intelligence of sheep or goats, which do not appear to be animals of noteworthy intelligence?

We were unable to discover any previous experimental study of learning in either the sheep or goat. However, Karl S. Lashley and Shephard I. Franz had published a report describing a simple maze of three parallel alleys in which they had investigated the effects of removal of parts of the brain on the learning ability of white rats. We constructed a similar maze for sheep. It was an outdoor structure with alleys eighty feet long. One of the outer passages was a blind alley. The mother sheep was tethered at the end of the maze, and the lamb's problem was to find its way up the center alley and down the open outer alley in order to join the mother to nurse. The number of trials required for the lamb to find its way through the maze without a mistake three times in succession was our criterion for the speed of learning or intelligence.

We began testing the intelligence of twin lambs at the age of about two weeks. The twin that proved the smarter was deprived of its thyroid. The mother and twins were then turned out to pasture for the summer. In the fall, four months later, the twins were tested again, this time with the maze in the original form and then with the position of the blind alley reversed.

The test failed to show any significant difference between normal and thyroidectomized sheep (four pairs were tested). Although the animals without thyroids were markedly dwarfed and sluggish, and waddled awkwardly along with frequent pauses, they found their way to the end of the maze as successfully as their normal twins.

We then made the problem more difficult. Each sheep was required to escape from the maze four times in succession, and the position of the blind alley was reversed at every trial. On the first trial the animal had to turn to the right, on the second trial to the left, on the third to the right, and on the fourth and final trial to the left again. No sheep or goat ever mastered this problem of the alternating maze. All made mistakes, occasionally on the third trial and more frequently on the last trial of the day. Again no significant differences were observed between the "cretin" dwarf and its normal twin, although eight of the sheep were tested three times a week for three years. Thus three years were spent in a fruitless attempt to demonstrate blunted mentality in sheep and goats from which the thyroid gland had been removed.

In experimental studies of animal intelligence, it often happens that the principal subject being investigated is the *experimenter's* intelligence. At least this proved to be so in our own case. During this frustrating three years of experimentation we were noting items of behavior which seemed of negligible importance at the time but which now appear of major significance in our present study of emotional behavior.

For example, we discovered by chance that a sheep deprived of its thyroid gland suffers a blunting of vigilance—that primitive sentinel activity which forces an animal to react instantly to the slightest change in its surroundings. We were observing twin sheep three years of age which for two years had been running the alternating maze. Neither had succeeded in mastering the correct sequence of turns. One day, as the normal sheep was correctly turning right at the junction of the three alleys on the third trial, a pistol was fired. The animal immediately jumped, remained tensely motionless for several seconds and then proceeded along the alley leading to the food. Her "cretin" twin was then tested, but the pistol shot elicited no observable reaction: she kept plodding along down the alley. The next day the "cretin" went through the test in her usual slow, deliberate manner, but when the normal twin came to the point at the third trial where the shot had been fired, she suddenly stopped, bleated and ran in the wrong direction.

The thyroidless sheep's failure to react to the shot is curiously suggestive of lobotomized human patients, who in the first weeks after the lobotomy operation also show "decreased vigilance." Carney Landis, reporting on studies of such patients by the Columbia-Greystone Associates, has said: "Psychosurgery patients are 'tame' . . . they have lost anguish. This tameness is the most astonishing fact that evolves from all frontal-lobe investigations." Our thyroidectomized sheep undergoing difficult conditioning similarly lack "anguish" and appear tame.

During our first experiments with sheep and goats, weeds and grass growing on the floor of the maze caused us much annoyance. An animal released from the starting compartment would start walking briskly down the center alley but would then interrupt its journey to nibble at stray tufts of vegetation—while an observer held a stop watch on the test. We covered the floor of the maze with cinders and weeded it daily, but the animals still found, or pretended to find, something to nibble at. The sheep even "grazed" on the bare cement floor of the laboratory indoors during difficult conditioning experiments. Similarly a goat in the maze test sometimes reared up on its hind legs and peered over the fence, though all was quiet and there was nothing new to see.

In his discussion of such activity in the case of the stickleback (see pages 26 to 34), N. Tinbergen applies the term "displacement behavior." When a situation becomes too stressful, the displacement activity may serve as an escape hatch from the emotional impact of the frustrating circumstances. G. V. Hamilton in his *Objective Psychopathology* described the reactions of animals and human subjects to an unsolvable problem: namely, finding the door to food in a row where the food was concealed each time behind a different door, determined by chance. A child of five persevered at this task for some time and then said to the experimenter: "I must go home now!" The Gestalt psychologists call such displacement behavior "going out of the field." Falling asleep is another manifestation of the same proclivity to escape emotion-provoking situations.

Another source of annoyance and frustration in our study of learning was the sheep's insistence on running through the maze for its own reasons—not for the reasons or "motives" that we attributed to it. We had supposed that the desire for food or to join the flock was the animals' only motivation for mastering the maze. But after many months spent in observing sheep attempting to learn the alternating maze we began to entertain grave suspicions about this. In spite of their invariable mistakes, the normal sheep seemed eager to run the maze day after day. The experimenter, on coming into the barn to start the day's work, would regularly find these animals clustered about the screen door leading to the maze, as children congregate around the ticket window for the Saturday afternoon movie. When they reached the food box at the end of the maze, they often did not tarry there. One mature ewe was always in a hurry for the next trial. At the food box she rubbed her snout along the surface of the oats perfunctorily, sometimes taking a small bite, and in one continuous wheeling motion rushed off to the starting gate again. This same ewe later had a lamb and was confined to a corner of the barn where she could nurse it. One day shortly after the lamb was born, we allowed her to enter the maze but kept the lamb in the barn. The lamb struggled to get through the screen door to its mother, bleating lustily. The mother ignored it and completed the usual four runs, never once approaching the screen door or bleating to her lamb. Her maze activity was completely absorbing.

This sheep obviously was not motivated to exercise her defective skill in the alternating maze either by a longing for the reward of food or by the promptings of a gregarious instinct. She ordinarily ate little or nothing from the box of oats, and we found that shutting out the sight of the flock by closing the wooden storm door to the barn did not startle or disturb her. We may conclude that the running of the maze was a self-rewarding activity which was also self-perpetuating.

This zest or "ambition" to exercise an acquired skill appeared lacking in the thyroidectomized sheep. They did not wait at the door in the morning, nor did they go back of their own accord for the next trial. To quote Landis again on the results of psychosurgery: "Many of the patients following the operation were less ambitious or less zealous in their approach to their everyday tasks, in their social relationships, and in their attitude toward life."

There is no intention to force a comparison here between the effects on behavior of thyroidectomy and of psychosurgery. The point is that we need not be too squeamish or rigid about avoiding the everyday language used in describing our own behavior when we seek to describe what our experimental animals are doing.

This brief account of maze learning in the sheep and goat concludes the first chapter in our story of conditioning and emotional behavior. That the thyroidectomized animals suffered "psychological" blunting was apparent even to a casual observer. But we could not demonstrate any blunting of intelligence, such as occurs in a human cretin, by the method of maze learning. At this point we decided to employ for our purpose Pavlov's method of the conditioned reflex. We arrived at this decision for compelling reasons, or so they seemed at the time.

From our point of view, we did not have adequate control of

the experimental situation. The sheep and goats in the maze were doing what *they* wanted to do, not what we wanted them to do. It irked us to be compelled to observe passively what the animal chose to do rather than to be able to make it do what we wanted. It was not pleasant, for example, on a cold winter's day to watch a lethargic sheep lie down in the snow at the junction of the alleys and remain there for almost an hour before proceeding on its way. Moreover, our central problem at the time was still the physiology of the thyroid gland, not learning.

At this juncture, in the spring of 1923, we invited to Ithaca a former Pavlov associate, G. V. Anrep, who was then lecturing at Columbia University. In his Ithaca lecture Anrep concluded his account of Pavlov's investigations with a description of an experimental neurosis produced in a dog as a result of its attempt to distinguish a circle as a signal for food from an oval figure signaling no food. When the oval signal approached a circle (with the long axis in the ratio of 9-to-7 to the short one), so that the dog no longer could distinguish the circle from the oval, it exhibited a dramatic emotional upset. It barked and squirmed in its harness and could not be quieted. The emotional disturbance persisted, and further tests had to be abandoned. This classical experiment is now well known, but Anrep's account gave us the first inkling of Pavlov's new interest in problems of psychiatry. Of more importance to us at the time, however, was his clear description of the conditioned reflex method itself—a physiological method for studying behavior.

The day after his lecture Anrep visited our physiological field station and advised us how to construct a simple conditioned reflex laboratory. The sheep and goats, as cud-chewing animals, salivate continuously; hence we were unable to study salivary conditioned reflexes. But we soon found that we could very easily establish a conditioned motor reflex in a sheep or a goat by coupling the sound of the metronome with a brief, mild electric shock to the foreleg. The animal flexed its leg vehemently in response to this electric shock—a shock so weak that we could scarcely feel it on the moistened finger tips. (We have never employed on animals an electric shock from which we ourselves could experience the slightest pain.)

Our new investigation of conditioned reflexes proceeded rapidly. Selected for study were three pairs of mature twin sheep, all of which had been subjected to long training in the alternating maze. The experiments proceeded as follows: A sheep was led onto a laboratory stand where it was held by loops suspended from an overhead beam. Electrodes were attached to one foreleg, and a metronome was placed behind the animal. The observer watched the animal through a window from an adjoining room without being seen. He started the metronome clicking once per second, and after a few clicks a mild electric shock was applied to the foreleg. The sheep's immediate response to its first experience of the shock was a violent struggle to escape. Soon, however, it gave up struggling and remained quiet but tensely poised on its stand. After five to ten repetitions of the metronome signal, always followed by shock, the sheep reacted to the metronome by pricking up its ears, then lowering its head and after two or three seconds tentatively lifting its foreleg from the platform once or twice. This conditioned reflex became more precise with further repetition. Meanwhile the unconditioned reflex to the shock itself was also becoming more precise. Instead of lunging forward vigorously in an attempt to escape, the animal came to react with only a brief, perfunctory flexion of the foreleg. After a hundred coincidences of metronome and shock a stable coupling was established in all six sheep, and the conditioned reflex to the metronome signal was both precise and predictable.

We believed that at long last we had mastered a method of study in which we had control over the sheep's behavior. The sheep had relinquished its initiative and remained standing quietly (often for as long as two hours), only flexing its trained foreleg in response to the experimenter's metronome signal or electric shock. The sheep's behavior had become stimulus-bound, and it behaved predictably. The self-rewarding, self-perpetuating activity that had occurred in the maze never appeared in this new experimental setting.

We found no significant differences between normal and thyroidectomized sheep, either in the rapidity with which the new reflex was formed or in its stability once it had been established. We also failed to discover any significant difference in their ability to discriminate between metronome rates. Both a normal sheep and its thyroidectomized twin could be trained to differentiate, for example, between a beat of 120 to the minute as a signal for shock and 84 per minute as a no-shock signal.

Once again no blunting of "intelligence" could be demonstrated. But the conditioned reflex method unexpectedly disclosed a striking difference in emotional behavior. This discovery, as is so often the case in behavior research, was made by accident. We had been training a pair of twin sheep on a task which Pavlov regarded as difficult for the dog; namely, the formation of delayed conditioned reflexes. The shock was timed to coincide with the sixth click of a one-per-second sequence on the metronome; in other words, the signal was not only the clicking but the clicking for exactly five seconds. After several days' tests both sheep began to delay flexing the leg until just before the shock. For example, the lifting of the leg might coincide with the fourth or fifth click. At this point we were impatient to obtain more data for a paper shortly to be presented at a scientific meeting, and to meet this deadline we abruptly doubled the animal's daily task. The sheep's schedule was increased from ten signals at each test session to twenty signals. On the second day of the doubled schedule the normal sheep became highly excited. It struggled violently at the signal and the shock, and during the intervals between signals it continued to execute small, jerky movements of the trained foreleg, like the uncontrollable twitching of the facial muscles in patients afflicted by tic. Moreover, the animal exhibited every evidence of alarm, including repeated movements of the head and ears, bleating, labored breathing and repeated micturition and defecation. The next day the sheep resisted being led to the laboratory, and although only five signals were given, its agitation was more pronounced than on the previous day. Even when the signals and shocks were eliminated from the daily session and the animal merely stood undisturbed on its stand with food in front of it, its agitation continued.

Meanwhile the thyroidectomized twin continued to execute precise delayed flexions of the trained foreleg even with its doubled burden of twenty signals per day. It came willingly to the laboratory and maintained its quiet deportment. It never exhibited the slightest sign of emotional excitement or alarm.

This laboratory accident of 1927 became a turning point in our research. We recalled Anrep's description of the experimental neurosis in Pavlov's dog and suspected that we had precipitated an experimental neurosis in the sheep by doubling its daily work load. Further investigation fully confirmed this suspicion. During the summer of 1929 Pavlov's senior assistant, P. S. Kupalov, was a guest in our laboratory, and he recognized the familiar signs of experimental neurosis in the sheep. From daily association with this able investigator we learned the intimate details of conditioned reflex procedures employed in Pavlov's laboratory and, more than this, gained an insight into the thinking and scientific aspirations of Pavlov and his co-workers.

For the past twenty-six years the work of our laboratory has centered on studying this phenomenon of chronic emotional disorder in sheep and goats. We soon found it possible to precipitate the experimental neurosis in any member of the flock by a simple training procedure; namely, subjecting the animal day after day to a rigid and unvarying pattern of 10-second signals, always followed by shock and separated by equal intervals of time, either two minutes or six minutes. We found, further, that the experimental neurosis, once established, was truly chronic and strikingly affected not only the animal's behavior in the laboratory but its mode of living in the barn and pasture twenty-four hours a day for the remainder of its life. Its life span did not appear to be shortened because of its emotional incapacity. (It is recognized that human psychoneurosis does not necessarily shorten the patient's life either.) Our first neurotic sheep, for example, lived thirteen-and-a-half years—the longest lifetime of any sheep we have had. It exhibited its agitated neurotic pattern of behavior up to the day before it died.

All of our neurotic sheep and goats exhibited undue sensitivity to any situations which seemed to imply danger. Even the most feeble and innocuous change in the environment, if sudden, elicited an exaggerated alarm reaction and preparation for flight. For several nights we counted the heart rates of the normal and neurotic sheep without disturbing them as they rested in the barn. From the chest piece of a stethoscope strapped to the animal a long, thick walled rubber tube conducted the heart sounds to the listening observer in a small shed outside the barn. A normal sheep's heart beat slowly and steadily throughout the night. By contrast a neurotic animal's heart rate was rapid and highly variable, with frequent irregularities (premature beats). The variability was in part occasioned by the usual night noises. When a lamb bleated or a windmill creaked, the neurotic sheep's sensitive heart immediately accelerated. No such changes in heart rate could be detected in the normal sheep.

The most significant disability of the experimentally neurotic sheep or goat thus far discovered is that it is incapable of dealing with a situation of actual danger in a realistic fashion. On several occasions dogs have invaded the pasture, and their victim invariably has been one of our neurotic sheep. The animal's neurosis so damages its gregariousness that while the other members of the flock escape together in one direction the neurotic animal flees in panic by itself. We have often witnessed this aberrant escape behavior when a photographer approached the flock in the barnyard. A few years ago two friendly basset hounds, laboratory pets, escaped from their paddock and made for a flock of our sheep clustered around the barn. All but one member of the flock ran off to the pasture. The one which did not was a neurotic sheep. A few minutes later we discovered her crouched on the barn floor with one foreleg extended. The dogs had chewed it to the bone. It so happened that the extended forelimb was the one that had been "trained." This sheep gave birth to a lamb a few weeks later, but she was unable to nurse it.

Freud once expressed the opinion that "thinking is an experimental dealing with small quantities of energy, just as a general moves miniature figures about over a map before setting his troops in motion." We at first mistakenly entertained a similar view of the nature of conditioning. The clicks of a metronome and a mild electric shock to the foreleg of an animal cause a coupling of hearing with muscle contraction. The process seems very simple—a kind of primitive thinking involving only small amounts of energy. But the error of this conception soon became apparent.

The fact that a trained sheep or goat stands quietly in its restraining harness in the conditioned reflex laboratory does not mean that it is placid and relaxed. Every animal during the first few days of training struggles to escape from its restraining harness. When it ceases to struggle, the animal has replaced the physical restraint of the harness with a self-imposed restraint; it is encased, in fact, in a "psychical strait jacket." Similarly in response to the electric shock it replaces its first energetic and diffuse movements with slight flexions of the leg. That the quiet pose and precise foreleg movements of the well-conditioned animal conceal a strong emotional undertow was clearly demonstrated on many occasions. For example, a sheep which had been trained for three years in the conditioned reflex laboratory was once placed in the harness, with electrodes attached to the foreleg, and kept there for the customary hour without being given the usual signals or shocks. After five minutes its respiratory rate was 41 per minute; by the end of the hour its breathing had become rapid and labored —135 per minute. As the hour progressed the sheep showed more and more evidences of restlessness: it made tentative movements of the trained foreleg, yawned and sometimes ground its teeth (the medical term is bruxism).

We were forced to the conclusion that the conditioned reflex described by Pavlov is not primarily an example of ordinary learning nor a manifestation of intelligence. It is, instead, primarily a manifestation of the emotional context of behavior. We now think of the conditioned reflex as an emotionally charged episode of behavior bracketed between two primitive, stereotyped reactions: the vigilance reaction (Pavlov's "What-is-it?" reflex) and the unconditioned reaction to the reinforcement of the conditioned stimulus (or signal) by food, bitters in the mouth or electric shock to the limb. The conditioned reflex is a special case of the emergency reaction of a cat in preparation for the supreme exertion of fighting for its life when menaced by a barking dog. It is an episode of emergency behavior in response to a stressful situation—a situation which arouses a persisting, apprehensive watchfulness on the animal's part, as demonstrated by the sheep standing in the harness for an hour waiting for the familiar conditioned stimuli which are withheld.

Paradoxically a negative conditioned stimulus, i.e., a signal indicating that no shock is to be given, is emotionally more disturbing to the sheep or goat than the positive signal. We have repeatedly observed that an uninterrupted series of negative conditioned stimuli results in experimental neurosis. When the dentist says:

"This may hurt a little," the patient may be more distressed if it happens not to hurt than if the pain comes as expected. Actual pain, when confidently anticipated, leads to relief of painful emotional tension.

This story of conditioning and emotional behavior can be concluded with a brief summary of our further investigations. In the first place, we have been able to abolish completely the neurotic manifestations of neurotic sheep simply by removing the thyroid gland. All signs of the "neurosis" disappear within a week after the operation. But the neurotic symptoms are fully reinstated if the thyroid hormone thyroxin is injected into the same sheep. It must be noted here that we have never succeeded in producing an experimental neurosis in a sheep or goat deprived of its thyroid.

In the course of our investigation more than fifty sheep and goats with experimental neurosis have been thoroughly studied. We have never found a permanent "cure" for their condition. As in human psychoneurosis, the chronic emotional disorder in these animals stubbornly resists treatment. We have tried the "rest cure," but keeping the animal out of the laboratory for as long as three years has yielded no benefit. We have also tried a change of scene, removing neurotic sheep to a new laboratory on a much larger farm, but their neurosis remained as before. Careful retraining with a lighter schedule ("change of job") also was of no avail.

Twenty years ago Frank Hartman of the University of Buffalo obtained some promising results in treating neurosis with injections of an extract of the adrenal cortex. His treatment so improved the condition of a bedridden psychoneurotic housewife that she was able to resume her household tasks. At the time, we tried injections of his extract of cortin, as he then called it, in three of our neurotic sheep. The extract had a noticeably calming effect on them. One neurotic sheep showed no signs of experimental neurosis for twenty-four days after the last injection. Since that time clinicians have made great progress in analyzing the role of hormones from the pituitary gland (ACTH) and from the adrenal cortex (cortisone, for example) in protecting individuals against environmental stresses. We are now about to resume our former study of the influence of these internal secretions on the experimental neurosis.

Nevertheless it seems to us that prevention is the best therapy. Our principal research objective, therefore, is to determine in detail what features of our training regimen are most stressful for our animals and in what specific ways we can increase their resistance to these stresses in order that neurotic breakdown may be avoided.

An eminent surgeon once said that he had never heard of anyone dying from overwork. It is worry over work that does the damage. Our sheep did not worry in the maze, but they did in the conditioned reflex laboratory. They gave evidence, through the disturbed and sensitive heart, of having taken their worries into the barn at night.

It is a commonplace of psychiatry that the most severe and disabling psychic injuries in patients are always found to have been inflicted in infancy or early childhood. Parents do not inflict these grievous injuries wittingly; the damage often results from rigid "moral" principles of child-rearing or by inadvertence. The consequent defects of character and personality are what the psychiatrist later has to deal with in attempting to restore his patient's usefulness and zest.

We now have an experimental flock of 50 sheep and 75 goats, all variously conditioned. For the past four years, with the aid of generous grants from the National Institute for Mental Health of the U. S. Public Health Service, we have been engaged in a program of research the aim of which is the prevention of "mental illness." We are pursuing this aim through an experimental analysis of a sheep or goat mother's ability to protect her offspring from environmental stress during its most vulnerable period of development. Once again the fortunate choice of the sheep and goat as experimental animals has been a big help, and for the same reason—the frequency of twins in these species.

A typical experiment will illustrate our mode of attack. The subjects are a mother goat and her twin kids of the same sex, aged three weeks. The experiment takes place in two identical rooms 10 feet by 10 feet. One of the pair of kids is confined in each room, the only difference being that one kid has its mother with it and the other is alone. Each kid wears a web strap which connects it by a flexible cable to a lever system on the ceiling, and electrodes run from the cable to its right foreleg. The little goat's locomotion is not interfered with: it may run, jump or even fall over backward without becoming entangled in the suspended cable. Its movements around the room during the test hour are recorded on a paper tape in a distant room and an observer also watches it, either from a corner in the room or from outside through a one-way screen.

Every two minutes the overhead lights are turned off, leaving just enough illumination to see the animal in the room. After ten seconds the lights come on again and a brief shock is applied to the little goat's foreleg. Twenty darkness signals are given each day, and the sequence of signals and shocks is automatically regulated by a clocking device.

The little animal in the room by itself invariably develops a certain pattern of behavior in response to the conditioned stimulus (darkness). It soon avoids the center of the room and moves cautiously along the walls. Later it limits its locomotion to one wall. Finally it comes to cower against the wall in one corner. Moreover, it develops the characteristic neurotic pattern exhibited by a goat trained in the conventional Pavlov restraining harness. But the twin in the other room, with its mother present, behaves quite differently. During the two-minute intervals between the darkness signals it moves freely around the room. Somehow the mother's presence protects the baby goat from the traumatic influence of the monotonously rigid pattern of tensions to which its twin in the adjoining room succumbs.

Perhaps the most instructive result of this experiment is the finding that these tensions impose on the isolated animal a psychic strait jacket almost as strong as a physical harness. It calls to mind the fact that a person who arrives at a railroad station a little early does not wander far but usually stands on the platform looking for the train to come.

We recently subjected to a followup test eight goats which had been conditioned in this manner as infants two years earlier. Had their early stressful experience left a "psychic trauma" in all eight goats, or had the four who were protected by the mother's presence been spared any emotional injury? To answer this question all eight animals were brought to the laboratory at the same hour every day for twenty days. They were held by restraining harnesses and at six-minute intervals for two hours were given ten-second "darkness" signals (dimming the lights in the room), with each signal followed by a shock to the foreleg.

By the twentieth day a definite answer to our question had been given. The four goats which had had their mothers with them during their early experience showed no evidences of abnormal behavior in response to the severe stress of the two-hour daily session. The other four exhibited the familiar signs of experimental neurosis.

In conclusion, we again insist that prevention is the best therapy. But prevention waits upon understanding. One avenue leading to this understanding is the one that we have been traversing. It is our belief that painstaking and continuing investigation of animal conditioning and emotional behavior will prove indispensable to that understanding of human mental health and disease upon which reliable preventive measures must depend.

CURIOSITY IN MONKEYS

by Robert A. Butler

CURIOSITY IS CERTAINLY one of the strongest motives in human behavior. Children begin very early to explore the world around them: they are excited by new sights and sounds, continually manipulate and investigate their toys or other small objects, and in general are extremely responsive to new things and events in their environment. Indeed, severe deprivation of environmental stimulation may permanently retard a child's development.

Until recently little or no research has been conducted on the curiosity motives, for reasons which are not hard to discover. A current theory in psychology has reduced human motivations to the biological drives of hunger, thirst and sex and the conditioned drive to avoid pain, and it has maintained that all learning is based on these drives. Curiosity was dismissed by the behaviorists as an "instinct," beyond the scope of experimental investigation. But in recent years psychologists have found a great deal of experimental evidence that the behavior of human beings and other primates cannot be explained adequately in terms of biological or pain-avoidance drives. Some experimental study has been given to the curiosity motives in monkeys, and this article will review those studies.

The everyday behavior of monkeys seems plainly to be motivated in considerable part by something akin to curiosity. Monkeys, not unlike children, persist in examining things in their immediate environment by close inspection and manipulation. Every object presented to a monkey is at one time or another handled, fondled, scratched, rubbed, bent, picked at, bitten and pulled apart before finally being discarded. A monkey will tamper with the lock on his cage door and will invariably confiscate any objects left on accessible shelves. In short, a monkey spends a considerable portion of his life "monkeying around" with anything he can get his hands on.

To prove that monkeys have a fundamental curiosity drive, or drive to manipulate, we must demonstrate three things: (1) that they will work for long periods with the manipulatory behavior itself as the sole reward; (2) that the manipulation drive will produce learning, in the same way as the hunger or pain-avoidance drives, and (3) that no drives other than curiosity are significantly influencing the experimental results.

Harry F. Harlow and his associates at the University of Wisconsin were the first to investigate manipulatory behavior in monkeys. Their experiments were designed to determine whether monkeys can learn how to solve a mechanical puzzle with no reward other than the working of it. The puzzle consisted of three interlocking devices—a metal pin, a hook-and-eye and a hasp. The three items could be disengaged if the monkey first removed the pin, then took the hook out of the eye and finally lifted the hasp. If the monkey touched any of the items out of order, it was counted as an error. After a few training sessions the monkeys' score was nearly perfect. Then the puzzle was made harder by adding more devices, but it was just as readily solved. Another study investigated the persistence of this behavior. Every six minutes the puzzle was reset. The monkeys went on disassembling it repeatedly for ten hours, at which point the experimenters, rather than the subjects, had had enough.

Recently Wisconsin's Primate Laboratory devised a puzzle that involves learning to discriminate between stimuli. The usual procedure in such a test is to give a reward, such as food, for the correct response in a choice between two different stimuli. But in this experiment the only reward was the opportunity to manipulate objects. Ten screw eyes were mounted in two vertical rows on a metal panel. Five of them, colored red, were removable; the other five, colored green, were firmly fixed. The screw eyes were randomly placed so that the only clue to whether they were removable was color. The monkeys soon learned that the red screw eyes could be removed to play with, and they almost unerringly touched only those.

These experiments yielded two important findings: that the opportunity to manipulate objects is reward enough to motivate monkeys to learn, and that an external stimulus, like an internal, biological one, can evoke a drive. The curiosity motives apparently are initiated by external stimuli.

What kinds of stimuli are most effective in eliciting the manipulation drive? Wallace Welker of the Yerkes Laboratories of Primate Biology has just completed experiments on chimpanzees which bear directly on this problem. On a table before the chimp's cage he placed a pair of objects. One of the pair would be movable and the other fixed, or the handling of one would produce a sound and the other not. Like monkeys, the chimpanzees showed a strong preference for movable objects over fixed ones and for objects that produced a sound or triggered a light over those that yielded no change in the environment. After thirty minutes with a pair of objects the animals became bored and stopped handling them, but their interest could be maintained if new stimuli were introduced periodically. Young chimpanzees consistently displayed more manipulatory behavior than older ones.

Monkeys and apes watch closely everything that goes on around them. Perhaps this expression of curiosity in monkeys accounts for their popularity with man. At the zoo or in the laboratory, man and monkey seem to observe each other with great interest. Which one derives more information from the experience remains an enigma. It is as if man as an observer meets his first real competitor in the monkey. Sometimes this competition becomes rather unnerving. I had such an experience during the course of a series of experiments at the Wisconsin laboratories. I was testing monkeys on a food-rewarded problem. The monkey worked behind a screen where it could not see the experimenter. By the same token, the experimenter could not see the monkey, and there was a great temptation to peek to find out what the animal was doing. I first made a small peephole in the panel, but the monkey quickly discovered it and thereafter spied on me as often as I did on him. I next tried placing a small mirror in a position that enabled me to watch the animal constantly. The monkey turned the tables by dropping its work and watching me through the mirror!

Taking advantage of this lead, we designed an experiment to investigate monkeys' visual exploratory behavior. The apparatus was essentially an enclosure with a built-in color discrimination problem. Monkeys were rewarded by a view of the surroundings outside the enclosure, provided they responded correctly on the problem. The monkey was placed in a large box with two doors. The animal was given preliminary training to familiarize it with the apparatus: first it was given a look through the open doors into the laboratory, where considerable activity was going on, and then the experimenter closed the doors. Soon the monkey learned to open the doors within a few seconds.

Then the main part of the experiment began. One door was locked, and it was identifiable by a yellow card on the inside. The other door, marked by a blue card, was unlocked. The experimenter raised a screen that had been lowered between the monkey and the doors, exposing the two doors with their differently colored cards. If the monkey pushed against the door with the blue card, the door opened and it could look outside. After 30 seconds the experimenter lowered the screen and the trial was over. If the animal pushed against the door holding the yellow card, it automatically flashed on a light which signaled its error; the experimenter immediately lowered the screen, denying the subject a glimpse of the outside world. Twenty trials a day were given for 20 days, and each test session lasted from 25 to 45 minutes. The experimenter recorded the number of correct responses and the length of time that elapsed between the raising of the screen and the monkey's attack on one of the doors. The speed of response provided a measure of the strength of the monkey's motivation to look outside.

The results of the experiment left no doubt about the strength of the monkey's curiosity or its power in promoting learning. Throughout the 20 days of testing the animals worked away eagerly at the problem (the colored cards were shifted at random from door to door). Without tiring of the game, they went on pushing the doors enthusiastically to get a look at the people working in the laboratory outside the box. In a second study that ran for 57 days and presented various color-discrimination problems, the subjects worked just as unflaggingly.

These data strongly suggest that the drive to explore visually is indeed a fundamental drive in monkeys. To measure its strength and persistence further, two monkeys were tested for four continuous hours each day for five days. The animals worked as fast on Day Five as they did on Day One. A second experiment yielded still more surprising results. Three monkeys were put to the door-opening test hour after hour, with 30 seconds between trials, until they quit. One monkey performed for 9 continuous hours, another worked for 11 and the third for more than 19 hours! The response time of this marathon performer was actually shortest during the final hour of the test.

That monkeys would work as long and as persistently for a food reward is highly unlikely. The tenacity and rapidity with which these subjects performed on the task of opening a door in order to see outside clearly indicated that the activities in the laboratory were extremely effective in exciting their curiosity.

To find out what specific kinds of visual stimuli excited them, we presented to the monkeys three different sights: a fellow monkey, an operating toy electric train and an array of fresh fruit and monkey chow. As a standard for comparison the test was arranged so that the monkeys would sometimes see nothing but an empty room. The apparatus was the same as before except that this time the box had only one door. Upon opening the door, the monkey saw a large chamber which contained a monkey, the running train, the array of food or nothing at all. The monkeys were allowed a five-second view, and the trials were repeated at ten-second intervals. Eight monkeys were tested thirty minutes a day, five days a week for a period of four weeks. Each week the visual incentive was changed. The strongest incentive turned out to be, not surprisingly, the sight of another monkey; the electric train ran a close second.

We next investigated the relative effectiveness of different sounds. A highly vocal monkey and the noise of the electric train were the incentives. Sometimes the subjects, after opening the door, could see the source of the sound, sometimes not. Ten of the youngest monkeys in the colony participated in the study. All of them opened the door frequently and rapidly, through five weeks of testing, irrespective of which sound they heard or whether they were rewarded with the sight of the sound-maker. Although the experiment failed to show any clear-cut differences among the incentives, it provided valuable evidence on the strength of the curiosity drive in young monkeys.

These researches with monkeys and apes are the beginnings of what promises to be a most fascinating and important area of investigation. The strong tendency of monkeys and apes to explore all things and situations provides an extremely serviceable mechanism for acquainting these animals with the intricacies of their environment. That this tendency is most marked in the younger animals suggests that the curiosity motives are largely responsible for the early and extensive learning which unquestionably contributes to the biological success of the primates.

THE YERKES LABORATORIES

by George W. Gray

FRONTING THE PUBLIC HIGHWAY near Orange Park, Florida, not far south of Jacksonville, is a parklike development enclosed by a high woven-steel fence topped with an electrified wire. It is occupied by a cluster of modern buildings, which include offices, laboratories, a library and other working quarters of a scientific establishment. But the center of interest is a housing development to which these quarters are adjuncts. For here live nearly three score chimpanzees, forming perhaps the most remarkable nonhuman community anywhere on earth. Most of the inhabitants were born on the premises, and from birth have been reared and observed with elaborate care. There is a nursery for the youngsters, a maternity ward for expectant mothers, a small hospital for the sick, and a collection of spick-and-span apartments, each consisting of an indoor "bedroom" with a connecting outdoor "living room" cage, for the general population.

On the morning we arrived at the Yerkes Laboratories of Primate Biology, the colony was unwontedly quiet, for the residents were all locked in their bedrooms while attendants cleaned their cages with hoses and mops. When the housekeeping was finished, life resumed its normal stir. The dark forms of the Messrs. and Mesdames Anthropoid appeared in the cages; an occasional raucous howl or shriek rent the air. We set out to get acquainted with the colony under the escort of Henry W. Nissen, associate director of the Laboratories, who cautioned: "You'll find some vigorous characters, and as many different personalities as there are chimpanzees."

Appropriately, the first cage was occupied by Alpha, the first animal to be born here. She celebrated her twenty-fifth birthday last September. Alpha was drowsing in the sunshine; at our approach she arose and thrust long fingers through the wide mesh of the steel screen. It was an exploratory gesture, also an invitation to come a little closer. Dr. Nissen held out his sleeve so that she could reach the cuff links. She bent to the task with complete concentration, her sensitive lips moving in unison with her fingers as she undid the links and loosened the sleeve. When we offered a pencil and a piece of paper, she took them and began a crude scribbling on the concrete floor. We provided a penny, thinking it might be useful for drawing a circle, but she slipped the coin into her mouth. When we looked in on her again an hour later, she had the pencil firmly clasped between the toes of her right foot and fragments of the paper clutched in her left foot. As she saw us, she pursed out her lips to display the penny.

Alpha is friendly, even-tempered, level-headed but not brilliant. Her mother died at her birth, and the four-pound infant was taken into the home of a member of the staff and raised there through her first year. She has been the subject of many psychological experiments. Alpha now weighs 140 pounds, is about four feet, four inches in height, and has the characteristic brown eyes and beetling brow-ridges of her species. Chimpanzees are born with blue eyes which change to brown in a few weeks.

Alpha's eldest offspring is Alf, now fourteen years old. He was in a nearby cage, dancing around and clapping his hands in a jovial effort to attract attention. Alf has inherited his mother's sunny disposition and is one of the most lovable and trusting apes of the Orange Park community. His maternal grandfather Pan was also a famous dancer and handclapper, so Alf comes by his showmanship naturally.

But the greatest clown of that morning tour was Ken. He is a husky fifteen-year-old, and as we approached he began a slow dance. Gradually the tempo speeded up until suddenly he leaped up, grasped a steel bar of the cage roof and drew himself up and down in a trapeze act, all the while bobbing his head in a comical way. After about a dozen of these contortions Ken dropped to the floor and crouched motionless, as though waiting for applause. During these gymnastics, Ken's consort Flora (a daughter of Alpha) sat quietly in a corner, as bored as any wife who has had to listen too often to the same joke.

The next cage housed Hal and Ami. As a child Ami was one of the most affectionate in the nursery, but during adolescence her personality changed radically, and now, at age eighteen, she is soured on the world. Nobody ever gets a welcoming gesture from Ami, and no one attempted any fingers-through-the-bars visiting with her. Hal's disposition is not much better. We stayed back from the cage, but, as it turned out, not far enough back, for suddenly Hal spat a six-foot stream of muddy water he had been saving for just such a target. We retreated to a washroom to swab off the spots, and then completed the tour without further mishap. Altogether we visited fifty-eight chimpanzees, including babies in the nursery.

It is in the laboratory tests that the chimpanzees' individual personalities come into sharpest focus. For example, Bokar, a cage exhibitionist who will boisterously slam his bedroom door back and forth to attract a visitor's attention, shows indifference to the human species when the chips are down. He will go through the rigmarole of a problem for the bit of banana or other food reward that awaits a successful performance, but don't expect from him any spirit of co-operation. There are other hedonists like Bokar—Soda and Helene are examples among the females—who are interested only in the loaves and the fishes. The extreme misanthrope is Bula, who hates all human beings—and the longer she has known man the sharper is her hatred. Bula has bitten more staff members than any other animal in the colony, but surprisingly she gets along well with fellow apes.

Some chimpanzees show stubborn streaks. Portia, an extremely keen problem solver, will frequently make a run of ten to eighteen correct solutions in a row, and then, right on the heels of this good performance, will perpetrate an unbroken run of errors. She calls the wrong turn so repeatedly that one can only conclude that she is missing purposely to foul up the experiment. In a different class from Portia, but equally difficult, is Rob. When the going is hard in a test, Rob will simply sit motionless, staring as in a trance. He has been known to huddle in one position for more than thirty minutes, with his legs extended and his arms rigid—a condition that approaches catalepsy in a human being. Indeed, some of the chimpanzees show behavior which a psychiatrist might call schizophrenic. They go through little rituals, crouching in a corner and rubbing a hand ceremoniously, or sitting motionless for hours in apparent catatonia—"just stir-crazy," as one staff man phrased it.

But many in the colony have a genuine liking for people, and these enter upon the tests with a seeming desire to work with the experimenter and to excel in performing the task. Wendy and her son Jed are of this type; so are Alpha and Alf and many others. They are warmnatured, openhearted, trustful and trustworthy—a pleasure to work with.

The chimpanzee colony is a world in itself—and mirrors traits which are all too familiar components of the human scene.

This unique outpost of biological research has been operating in the Florida savanna since 1930. The idea had been born thirty years earlier when Robert M. Yerkes, then twenty-six and a graduate student and instructor in psychology at Harvard University, began to dream of an institute where he could study the total biologic and psychic development of animals in relation to the environment. He conceived that the most useful subjects would be members of the order of primates, particularly the great apes, and he set out to learn all he could about these animals. Little was then known about them, and Yerkes traveled about to make personal observations at first hand in zoos and private collections. One of the largest collections was that of a wealthy Cuban woman, Madame Rosalia d'Abreu, who had assembled some eighty apes and monkeys on her estate near Havana. When she learned of Yerkes' interest, Madame d'Abreu invited the scientist to visit her pets. He spent several months there in systematic study. Chimpanzees seemed by all odds the most promising material for psychobiological research. They were more tractable than gorillas, more alert and co-operative than orangutans. In the summer of 1923 Yerkes bought two young chimps, recent arrivals from the Belgian Congo. He took them to his farm in New Hampshire, and within a few weeks they had won places for themselves in the household—but alas! before a year had gone Panzee was dead of tuberculosis and Chim of pneumonia.

Yerkes outlined his idea for an institute in a letter to *Science* in 1916 which evoked much interest, but not until 1924, when he was appointed to a professorship at Yale University, did he obtain backing for his dream. Yale agreed to include a primate laboratory in its Institute of Psychology, and the Rockefeller Foundation soon afterward voted $40,000 for a four-year test of Yerkes' idea—the first of its continuing subsidies for the project.

The mortality of chimpanzees in captivity had been so great that many authorities doubted that a colony could be maintained to permit sustained research. The first task therefore was to determine whether or not the animals could be kept under conditions of experimental control. A few days after the Rockefeller grant was received, a ship bringing five young chimpanzees from Sierra Leone docked in Brooklyn. Yerkes, notified by telegraph, hurried to look them over and selected a three-year-old male and a four-year-old female, for which he paid $1,200. (The ages, of course, were only estimates.) This was the summer of the famous Scopes trial in Tennessee, in which William Jennings Bryan prosecuted a young high-school instructor for teaching Charles Darwin's theory of evolution, contrary to the law of the commonwealth. Yerkes named the male chimp "Bill," after the prosecuting attorney, and the female "Darwinia," soon shortened to "Dwina."

Bill and Dwina thus have the distinction of being the first "settlers" of the Yale anthropoid colony. They spent the summer on the Yerkes farm in New Hampshire. In September they were joined by another pair of chimps purchased from a ship's officer, who had picked them up in a West African port and was so fed up with the supervision of his pets by the time the ship reached Boston that he was glad to sell the two for $500. They were promptly named "Pan" and "Wendy," after the *Peter Pan* characters.

A brick barn on Prospect Street in New Haven was remodeled to house the four apes, and there it was soon demonstrated that the rearing of chimpanzees was feasible and the use of them in scientific research practicable. Before the four years were up, Yerkes began to look for a permanent site for the laboratory, and he decided it should be located in a more tropical climate. A survey committee of eminent biologists endorsed the expansion, and the Rockefeller Foundation appropriated additional funds to purchase a 200-acre tract at Orange Park, to erect buildings and equipment and to meet operating expenses of the laboratory for ten years.

The new buildings were completed in the spring of 1930. The architect turned them over to the University on June 9, and the following day Bill, Dwina, Pan and Wendy arrived from New Haven. Dwina was pregnant and the staff was looking forward to the first birth in the colony. It occurred on September 11, when the baby Alpha was successfully delivered. Dwina, however, contracted puerperal septicemia and died two weeks later—the first recorded case of childbed fever in an anthropoid ape. Her pregnancy had afforded the first systematic observation of a chimpanzee's reproductive process from conception to birth. The ape's gestational period was determined to be 245 days, compared with 280 days for a human mother.

Gifts and additional purchases of animals, plus the returns from a gradually rising birth rate, increased the size of the colony. By 1941, when Yerkes retired as director, the laboratory population totaled forty-five. It was by far the largest collection of chimpanzees that had ever been assembled for use in scientific work, and the fact that more than half of them had been born in Orange Park was a testimonial to the success of the breeding program. The colony had grown in usefulness and in research results as well as in numbers. In 1942 the station was incorporated separately and named, in honor of its founder, the Yerkes Laboratories of Primate Biology. It ceased to be a division of Yale and was sponsored jointly by Yale and Harvard. Karl S. Lashley, professor of neuropsychology at Harvard, was appointed to succeed Yerkes as director, under a supervisory board of scientists.

"Compared with other laboratory animals, chimpanzees are expensive, not only in cost of maintenance but also in the time required for an investigation," says Lashley. "Their use is justified only in studies for which they have a unique value, and a major task of my office is to identify the problems for which these animals are the preferred subjects. Thus far the main investigations have been in the fields of cerebral function, comparative intelligence and sex physiology. Exploratory studies indicate that the apes may also be useful for the investigation of nutrition, aging, personality and psychopathology."

Asked to name the most important single contribution that has come from research in the Laboratories, Lashley answered that he would unhesitatingly select "Carlyle Jacobsen's discovery of the reduction of temper tantrums in chimpanzees by brain lesions." This discovery, which led to the human operation of prefrontal lobotomy, is indeed a landmark in modern neurological history. It provides a striking example of the unique value of the chimpanzee in certain fields of medical experimentation.

Jacobsen was a member of the Yerkes staff from 1930 to 1937 (he is now executive dean for medical education in the University of the State of New York). He was interested in psychoneurology, and a great deal of his work was focused on the function of the frontal lobes of the brain. When the research involved surgery, he had the collaboration of John F. Fulton, neurosurgeon and professor of physiology in the Yale Medical School.

In 1933 a study was begun with two chimpanzees of very different temperaments. Lucy was a calm and even-tempered six-year-old; Becky, a year or so younger, was an excitable neurotic who fell into a rage whenever she made a wrong choice in a test. Jacobsen made various tests of the two chimps' learning ability and memory. Then by a delicate operation he and Fulton cut out about half of the prefrontal area from each animal's cerebral hemisphere. After the wounds had healed, the intelligence tests were repeated, and the animals reacted pretty much as before—Lucy with deliberation and composure, Becky with tantrums when she failed to solve a problem and obtain the food reward. The experimenters then made the operation more radical: they removed the remaining half of the forepart of each animal's brain. In the case of high-strung Becky this produced an astonishing change. She was no longer annoyed when she made the wrong choice; she merely shrugged her shoulders and went on to the next test, quite indifferent to failure or disappointment.

Jacobsen and Fulton reported this experiment at an international medical conference in England in 1935. The Portuguese neurologist Egas Moniz expressed great interest in Becky's changed behavior. It suggested, he said, that anxiety states in men and women might be relieved by surgical means. And within a year Moniz, in collaboration with a Lisbon surgeon, had operated on fifty hopeless mental patients in Portugal. They did not remove tissue, as had been done with the apes, but severed the pathways between the prefrontal region and the brain stem by skillfully cutting the connecting nerve fibers. A fair percentage of the fifty patients reported relief from obsessions, fears, anxieties and other compulsive states. Other surgeons took up the operation, and at latest accounts it is said to have assisted several thousand psychotic persons in many countries toward a more tranquil life.

"If the influence on the development of 'psychosurgery' ascribed to Jacobsen's experiment is correct," said Lashley, "then this single study has been worth more, in terms of the usual cost and returns of psychiatric research, than the entire investment in the construction and maintenance of the Yerkes Laboratories."

The great value of Orange Park, the director went on, is not in spectacular discoveries but in the steady accumulation of data on fundamental problems. "Basic conceptions of instinct and of the nature of learning have been significantly modified, I think, by work done at the Laboratories. The studies of cerebral function have contributed to the development of an experimental attitude among clinical neurologists, as is illustrated by the Greystone project in New Jersey, with its systematic appraisal of the overall effects, both good and bad, of prefrontal lobotomy."

Jacobsen's pioneering experiments were followed by other investigations of the great roof of the brain—the cerebral cortex. It is a structure which man shares with the chimpanzee, the monkey and other anthropoids. The human cortex is about three times as large as the chimpanzee's, which in turn is double or triple that of the monkey, but in each primate the familiar landmarks are found: a general division of the cortex vertically into two hemispheres, and subdivisions of each hemisphere into certain regions —the occipital lobe at the rear, the parietal lobe just above it, the temporal lobe at the side and the frontal lobe under the forepart of the skull.

Neuropsychology is Lashley's specialty, and since he came to Orange Park its studies of cerebral function and neurological structure have been conducted under his personal direction. Two examples suggest the scope and pertinence of this research.

The first is the study of "associative areas"—regions lying between the sensory and motor centers of the cortex. These associative areas are supposed to be the "storehouses of memory." It had been observed, for example, that patients with tumors or injuries in these areas often suffered agnosia—loss of the ability to recognize objects by touch, vision or sound. When Lashley took up his duties at Yerkes, few experimental studies of the associative cortex had been reported, and he decided to concentrate on this part of the brain. Since monkeys would serve for most problems, he confined the experiments to them except in explorations of the prefrontal cortex, where chimpanzees were used.

The results have been surprisingly negative. The monkeys were first trained in specific discriminatory habits: for example, in using the sense of touch, to choose a prism and reject a cylinder if both were smooth, but to grasp the cylinder and reject the prism if both were rough. When the animals had learned this lesson, portions of the associative area of the parietal lobe were removed from their brains. It was found that the monkeys discriminated between prism and cylinder quite as well as before the operation. A similar test was made of their discrimination between colors, and again injury to the associative area of the visual cortex failed to impair the animals' memory of the choice of colors. It was only when the temporal lobes were completely excised that serious defects showed up in vision and touch; partial removal had little effect. Similarly, the five chimpanzees whose prefrontal lobes were removed showed no loss of memory or learning ability.

"It seems clear," says Lashley, "that current conceptions of the function and mode of action of these so-called associative areas are due for a drastic revision. They are not 'storehouses of memory,' nor do they appear to have localized functions. Any part of the cortical region seems capable of carrying out the functions of the whole. Studies by my associate, Kao Lang Chow, have shown, for example, that the same nerve cells in the primary visual cortex that retain visual memories are also continually active in other functions connected with seeing."

Another project in neurological research with important human implications is focused on brain scars. The Navy is financing this study, because it is naturally interested in brain damage from wounds. Neurologists know that while a sizable portion of the human brain may be cut out without apparent ill effects, a very small lesion, such as a cut or a compression, may cause severe trouble—epilepsy, paralysis, agnosia. At the Yerkes Laboratories Paul J. Hutt and Hiroshi Odoi, under Lashley's direction, have performed scarring operations on thirty-eight monkeys, using thirteen different ways of inflicting injury. Only one produced any obvious change in behavior. A small lesion in the left convolution at the top of the temporal lobe caused severe disorganization of the animal's responses to stimuli. The location of the sensitive area has been pinpointed, and Hutt and Odoi plan to explore the matter further.

In 1939 Nissen began a long-term study of the physical and behavioral development of chimpanzees. He has been assisted by numerous associates over the years, and the research results fill many volumes of notes. In consequence of this study, more is known of the growth and development of the chimpanzee than of any animal below man, with the possible exception of the laboratory rat.

Sixteen infant apes, including several pairs of brothers and sisters, were separated from their mothers soon after birth and installed in the nursery, where they could be under continuous observation. Thirteen have now been followed into maturity. During this long period they were regularly measured, photographed, X-rayed and tested for pulse rate, heartbeat, respiration rate and other characteristics. In addition, the growth and development of other infants were followed somewhat less intensively.

The studies show that the physical growth curve of the chimpanzee fairly well parallels that of the human being, although man on the average is larger and heavier. Detailed comparison of the growth of the chimpanzee with that of other animals and man may lead to a surer understanding of the interrelations in the growth of different parts of the body, as determined by heredity and as modified by environmental factors.

The study also includes a systematic observation of the sexual cycle, the time of ovulation and the pattern of sexual physiology and behavior. The influence of sex hormones on the temperament of primates has been investigated; the experiments show that dominance and aggressiveness increase under the influence of male hormones and decrease with female hormones. The program offers an opportunity to explore instinctive elements in sex behavior which it is believed may be generalized to man. Studies of pubescent individuals indicate that the chimpanzee's sex patterns are less stereotyped than those of lower animals.

The oldest chimp at Orange Park whose birth date is precisely known is Alpha, now aged 25. Wendy, bought by Yerkes in 1925, was estimated to be two years old then, which would make her 31. There is a still older member of the colony: Pati, a former pet of Madame d'Abreu who was presented to the Laboratories in 1931, is estimated to be 34. Nissen believes that the life span of the chimpanzee approaches that of man—somewhere between 50 and 60 years. Another quarter century at Yerkes should provide the answer.

In their study of the behavioral development of the chimpanzee, the Yerkes psychologists have attempted to follow their subjects with the same kind of observations that Arnold Gesell has made of the human infant. They have recorded such items as postural control, sensory-motor development, the beginnings of play, of social behavior and of more complex adaptive behavior. The investigators—Austin Riesen, Elaine Kinder and others—have found that the young chimpanzee develops more rapidly than a human infant in sensory and motor co-ordination, but it falls progressively behind in perceptual and manipulative ability. The ape's tendency to explore with lips and tongue rather than with the hands seems significant.

Yerkes says that he has never known a chimpanzee who was naturally and persistently unsociable. "Even in its relations with human beings a young ape shows impressive friendliness once its timidity and natural caution have been replaced by confidence and trust," he observes. Chimpanzee youngsters readily accept other animals on friendly terms as playmates, but if the other animal shows fear it is almost certainly in for trouble. In his book *Chimpanzees,* Yerkes tells of putting a woodchuck in a large room with a five-year-old chimpanzee. "All might have gone well if the woodchuck had stood its ground when the chimpanzee approached. Instead, it scurried away, chased by the ape. Before long both became excited and began to use teeth and claws defensively. To save the woodchuck for later experimental use, it was necessary to remove it. One lesson is clear. If an animal is to get along with a chimpanzee, it must stand its ground calmly when approached, since retreat or other show of timidity encourages pursuit and aggression."

Instances of co-operation are numerous. On one occasion a caretaker brought some grape juice for Josie, a chimp who a few hours before had given birth to a baby. Josie took the grape juice in her cupped lower lip, but instead of swallowing it she turned to Wendy, who was watching expectantly in the next cage, and poured the lipful of juice into Wendy's extended lip. She did this again and again until the caretaker's cup was almost empty.

Then there is the story of how Moos, a youngster who had been ill, helped his "doctor." Because he was refusing hard foods, a staff member decided to examine Moos's teeth. The young ape co-operated fully, opening his mouth wide and allowing the examiner to probe wherever he wanted to. When, finding nothing wrong, the examiner turned to leave, Moos pulled the man back, raised his upper lip and pointed to an area of his upper jaw. Sure enough there was a slight swelling, and subsequent examination showed that a permanent tooth was in process of eruption.

Easter (born on Easter Sunday, 1949) began at an early age to show a mechanical turn of mind and a remarkable proficiency in escaping from his cages. One day an investigator took Easter out to train him in some learning tests. He locked in Easter's cage mate, Lad, to keep him from interfering with the experiment. Lad protested, whimpering and scratching on the locked door. Easter soon went to his rescue. Although the lock was an unfamiliar one —a long bolt passed through two eyes and secured by a nut screwed on the end—Easter soon unscrewed the nut and freed his chum.

Nissen tells of a female chimpanzee who picked an attendant's pocket of his bunch of keys, tried the keys in the lock one after the other, finally hit on the right one and let herself out. After a half-hour exploratory tour of the grounds, she apparently became bored and allowed herself to be lured back. "It is almost certain," says Nissen, "that this animal had had no previous experience in the use of keys."

Chimpanzees habitually serve one another in the ritual of grooming. This is sometimes called "flea-picking," but erroneously, for a flea would find it difficult to get a footing on these sharp-eyed, sensitive animals, which daily examine their own skins and one another's in the search for foreign particles, pimples, abrasions, bits of loose skin and other excrescences. There is evidence that being allowed to groom is esteemed as great a privilege as being groomed. While grooming is primarily an act of toiletry, it often involves therapeutic services: the chimps extract splinters and other particles embedded in the skin, cleanse wounds and soothe injuries. Yerkes believes that grooming in the chimpanzee "represents a genetically important pattern of social response from which may have evolved some of our forms of social service." It may be a "forerunner of human hair and skin dressing, nursing, medical and surgical treatment."

The extent to which intelligent behavior is dependent on experience has been studied at Orange Park in various ways. One procedure has been to deprive subjects of practice in the use of a sensory faculty for a long time. Thus twelve chimpanzees have been raised in darkness. Snark and Alfalfa, a male and a female, were placed in a darkened room soon after birth and kept there, with the usual diet and care, for sixteen months. When they were brought out, their eyes showed sensitivity to light but were unable to respond to complex patterns. Eventually, after many months, Alfalfa developed recognition of objects, but Snark's sight progessively dimmed and finally failed completely. Examination indicated that the optic nerve had degenerated. Tests with other chimpanzees showed that if an infant is allowed only an hour and a half of light each day, this brief daily use of its eyes is sufficient to develop sight.

"It appears," said Nissen, "that the improvement in seeing ability which takes place progressively from birth up to about five months is a matter of practice in seeing objects. We kept an infant chimpanzee under a plastic dome which gave unpatterned light but did not provide any objects or images to look at—and found that this animal was almost as badly off as those raised in total darkness. The ability to see is not an inherent endowment, but has to be learned through experience."

There have been other deprivation experiments, and each confirmed the conclusion that perceptual faculties do not come with the mere presence of sense organs but are acquired through use.

Suppose that one were to go to the other extreme and, instead of restricting a chimpanzee's experiences, give it the rich experience of upbringing in a human household as a member of the family. This experiment has been made by several researchers at Orange Park. One baby chimp lived in a home for a year, another for nine months, another for two and a half years. But far and away the most important "adoption" was that of Viki, born on August 28, 1947. Immediately after birth she became the subject of an experiment which was destined to last nearly seven years, to pile up an unprecedented wealth of information and pictorial records, and to make her the most engaging ape in the history of primate research.

When Keith J. Hayes completed his postgraduate work in psychology at Stanford University in the spring of 1947, he and Mrs. Hayes had a clear idea of what they wanted to do. As she recorded it in her book, *The Ape in Our House*: "If we ever found the opportunity we would adopt a newborn chimpanzee and raise it as a human in all respects, giving it everything the human child needs: loving care, security, playmates, toys and sympathetic guidance. We decided that such a chimpanzee must be observed constantly for its entire life span. During its course of development, its body and brain must be compared not only with human beings its own age, but also with caged apes. The home-raised chimpanzee would provide psychologists with an evaluation of basic anthropoid intelligence, and, in addition, its unique upbringing would prepare our subject for many studies never before possible."

Dr. and Mrs. Hayes did not have to wait long for the opportunity. Soon after he got his Ph.D. the young psychologist was offered an opening at Yerkes and told that an infant chimpanzee would be provided. Viki, the daughter of Vera and Bokar, was three days old when Mrs. Hayes first saw her in the Yerkes nursery. The sight startled her. The newborn baby "looked like a monstrous spider, with long skinny arms and legs thrashing out from a solid potbelly. Most of her scant four pounds was concentrated in that middle, which was topped by an adhesive-tape navel dressing. The skin of her body was light brown, taut and shiny-smooth."

Six years of nurture and training in the Hayes home converted Viki into an 80-pound bundle of habits, skills and reasoning. She was able to match six-year-old children in solving many discrimination problems. She turned the switch of the electric fan, and when it failed to go on, she checked the wall socket and plugged in the wire. When a lamp remained dark after she had turned the switch, she removed the bulb and screwed in a fresh one. She wielded the carpet sweeper, dialed the telephone, applied her ear to the clock. The ticking of timepieces fascinated her, and once they found Viki on the floor holding her ear to a magazine picture of a watch.

At the age of three Viki performed with appropriate skill on such problems as form boards, peg boards, picture puzzles, block piling and buttoning. She solved problems which involved obtaining a prize by throwing a ball to knock it down, by pushing it out of a tunnel with a stick, by burning a string with a candle flame, by operating a light switch on the wall which released the prize magnetically from the ceiling, or by turning three levers in a certain sequence to open a box. The tests were given to four human children of the same age, and they excelled Viki only in the solution of the lever problem. A laboratory chimpanzee, nine months older, was completely baffled by all the tests except the one in which a ball was thrown to knock down the reward.

The one area in which the observers found Viki clearly and substantially inferior to human children was in language ability. "Although Viki learned to say a few words by the time she was three years old," explained Hayes, "she learned them with great difficulty, and the nature of her difficulty was significant. As an infant she babbled much less than human babies do, and even this vocalization had disappeared by five months of age. Since it appeared unlikely that she would speak spontaneously, we began a speech training program. The first step was aimed at teaching her merely to vocalize on command. The task was surprisingly difficult. It took her five months to learn to produce a hoarse staccato grunt, and it was quite unlike her normal spontaneous sounds.

"By manipulating Viki's lips we were able to make her say 'mama.' She learned to make the proper mouth movements herself and then was able to say 'mama' unaided—softly and hoarsely, but quite acceptably. By the time she was two and a half years old she had learned to pronounce approximations of the whispered words 'papa' and 'cup.' We did not manipulate her mouth in teaching these words, but simply insisted that she copy our example of a certain combination of play sounds. She soon learned to address the proper experimenter as 'mama' or 'papa' and to say 'cup' when she wanted a drink."

Several years ago Dr. and Mrs. Hayes ventured this diagnosis: "When Viki is compared with various human individuals who display a similar degree of language deficiency, we find that she bears little resemblance to those whose trouble is caused by feeble-mindedness or by abnormality of speech organs. But in certain respects she appears to resemble those cases, known as aphasics, whose deficiency is caused by abnormal brain structure, congenital or acquired. Like many aphasics, Viki is deficient in language comprehension as well as in speech, though here the deficit is less striking."

Even so, her powers of communication seemed remarkable. We visited her one afternoon in the yard of the Hayes home, about a mile from the Laboratories. Hayes, not present at first, arrived later in his car. As he drove up, Viki immediately began to click her teeth together. "That's her word for 'Let's go riding,'" Hayes explained, and answered, "All right." From the fenced-in yard she bounded through the house and emerged a few seconds later from the front door. After she had hopped into the car, Hayes said: "Close the window." Viki turned the handle and wound the window up about half way. "All the way," he commanded, and she wound it all the way.

She had other ways of communicating. "In her younger days," explained Hayes, "we used to carry extra diapers on automobile rides: so, when she wanted to go riding, she would bring a handful of diapers. After we removed the diapers from the bathroom, she brought a handful of cleansing tissue instead. A few evenings ago she began to tease for a ride. She clicked her teeth. Then she brought the tissue. I thought I would make her work a little harder, so I said, 'All right, if you get my scarf.' I had hung the scarf on a bathroom hook, but wasn't sure that Viki knew. She went directly to the bathroom, brought the scarf and started wrapping it around her neck. I said, 'No, put it on me.' And she did. Then I told her to get the door key. She had often led me to the desk, opened the drawer and pointed to the key, but she had never before actually taken it. Now she went instantly and brought the key. Then we went for our ride."

Another kind of communication is pictorial. "We can convey a message to her by drawing a picture, but Viki has shown no ability to draw pictures herself. Yet she has a fondness for mechanical things, and not only uses tools but invents them. This has always occurred in the realm of play. Once she noticed that an empty condensed-milk can rattled—there was a bit of loose solder inside. Later, having lost this can, Viki dropped a small hairpin through the hole of another can and made a rattle. On another occasion she made a sort of eolithic ax. While she was in the yard playing with a brick, the brick broke, leaving a nice sharp edge.

She used this piece for digging, pounding and cutting. Viki has used screwdrivers, hammers, saws, sandpaper and every sort of household tool. If the accustomed can opener won't work on an unfamiliar container, she is able to adapt to another tool and get the job done. She can handle things very precisely, pick up quite small objects and use fingers and thumb in opposition. She seems to appreciate fully such qualities as the strength of materials, weight and balance. I have seen her set a cup on the table, then notice that it is dangerously near the edge and move it to a safe position."

Our visit to Viki was on March 26 of last year. She was the picture of robust health, and in fact had grown so strong that a small cottage had been fitted up for her. There were a refrigerator, a dining table, can openers, electric fans—all her beloved gadgets. The plan was to install her there in May, supervising and observing her during the day and leaving her to sleep alone at night. But Viki never got there—and the cottage stands vacant and idle.

She was taken sick in late April, and in the course of the next three weeks physicians attended her. She was under barbiturate sedation during part of her illness, and on May 4 was given a transfusion of human blood—type O Rh-negative—with no ill effects. Despite 24-hour-a-day nursing she gradually grew weaker and on May 11 succumbed to epidemic encephalitis.

When chimpanzees at Orange Park need medical or surgical attention, a physician is called, for veterinarians are not trained in the ape's near-human anatomy and physiology. On one occasion a heavy steel slide fell on a chimpanzee and broke its left arm and pelvis. The chimpanzee was laid on a stretcher, put under anesthesia and taken by ambulance to a Jacksonville hospital. There, with five doctors and eight nurses in attendance, the broken humerus was set, and then the patient, still under anesthesia, was returned to the Laboratories. No one outside the group that attended him knew that the covered figure from Orange Park was not a human patient.

While the mortality rate at Orange Park has steadily declined in recent years, Viki's was the 62nd death, and the second caused by encephalitis. Dysentery and pneumonia have been the most frequent causes of death, but there has been a wide range of diseases; it appears that chimpanzees are susceptible to all the ills that man himself is heir to. This fact makes the animal of strategic value to medical research. Members of the colony have been used in extensive studies of bacillary dysentery and infantile paralysis; the polio investigation, which was carried on at the Yale Medical School, has involved a dozen of the more than fifty chimpanzees born at Yerkes in the last ten years. A study of the effects of body radiation was recently begun at Orange Park under a contract with the Atomic Energy Commission. This research is seeking to determine what effects radiation may have on behavior and, if possible, to differentiate between general symptoms (such as postradiation nausea) and direct effects on the central nervous system. Ten chimpanzees, ranging from infants to mature adults, are the subjects.

Lashley is hopeful that the chimpanzee will be useful for exploring problems of human genetics. L. H. Snyder, the well-known human geneticist of the University of Oklahoma, spent two weeks at Orange Park studying differences among the animals in relation to their parentage. He suggested that selective breeding be used to develop distinct races differing in measurable physical or behavioral traits, and that these races then be crossed for study of genetic patterns. A program of this kind would extend over many generations. But it seems practicable, if funds for such a long-term project become available. The physical data accumulated on inherited characteristics such as skin pigmentation and body proportions, when combined with data on behavior, should provide material for a genetic analysis, especially if combined with a comparative study of racial types of chimpanzees in nature.

Warren Weaver of the Rockefeller Foundation has playfully suggested that research at the Yerkes Laboratories may not be unilateral. As to this we can only speculate, but irrespective of whether or not the chimpanzees are also studying the scientists, there can be no doubt that the Yerkes scientists are deeply absorbed in their subjects. The intricate variety and daily surprises of the research material are endlessly stimulating. Every hall of science is, of course, a place of preoccupation—the focus of adventurous curiosity, enthusiasm and dedication. But while there are hundreds of laboratories studying rats, dogs, guinea pigs and other conveniently available organisms, in all the world there is only one laboratory colony of the sensitive, near-human, almost embarrassingly intelligent chimpanzees—in other words, only one Orange Park.

BIBLIOGRAPHY

READERS interested in further reading on the subjects covered by the chapters of this book may find the list below helpful. It is *not* a bibliography of source material. The books chosen are, for the most part, addressed to the general reader; they include also some of the more accessible textbooks and survey volumes. (The date given in italics under each chapter title is the date of its original publication in SCIENTIFIC AMERICAN.)

THE SPIDER AND THE WASP
August 1952

"Tarantula versus Tarantula-Hawk: A Study in Instinct." Alexander Petrunkevich in *The Journal of Experimental Zoology,* Vol. 45, No. 2, pages 367–397; July 5, 1926.

SEA LAMPREY AND LAKE TROUT
April 1955

"Feeding Mechanism of the Sea Lamprey and Its Effects on Host Fishes." Robert E. Lennon in U. S. Fish and Wildlife Service *Fishery Bulletin,* Vol. 56, pages 247–293; 1954.

Natural History of the Sea Lamprey, Petromyzon Marinus, in Michigan. Vernon C. Applegate. U. S. Fish and Wildlife Service, 1950.

Use of Electricity in the Control of Sea Lampreys: Electromechanical Weirs and Traps and Electrical Barriers. V. C. Applegate, B. R. Smith and W. L. Nielsen. U. S. Fish and Wildlife Service, 1952.

THE COURTSHIP OF ANIMALS
November 1954

King Solomon's Ring: New Light on Animal Ways. Konrad Lorenz. Thomas Y. Crowell Company, 1952.

Social Behavior in Animals: with Special Reference to Vertebrates. N. Tinbergen. John Wiley & Sons, Inc., 1953.

The Study of Instinct. N. Tinbergen. Oxford University Press, 1951.

THE CURIOUS BEHAVIOR OF THE STICKLEBACK
December 1952

The Study of Instinct. N. Tinbergen. Oxford University Press, 1951.

THE HOME LIFE OF THE SWIFT
July 1954

"The Breeding Behavior of the Swift." D. and E. Lack in *British Birds,* Vol. 45, No. 6, pages 186–215; June, 1952.
"The Breeding Biology of the Swift Apus Apus." D. and E. Lack in *The Ibis,* Vol. 93, No. 4, pages 501–546; October, 1951.

THE LANGUAGE OF THE BEES
August 1948

The Golden Throng. Edwin W. Teale. Dodd, Mead, 1945.
Sinnesphysiologie und "sprache" der Bienen. Karl von Frisch in *Naturwissenschaft,* Jahrg. 12, pages 918–993; 1924.
Bees: Their Vision, Chemical Senses and Language. Karl von Frisch. Cornell University Press, 1950.

THE ARMY ANT
June 1948

"Mass Organization in the Swarm-Raider." T. C. Schneirla in *Journal of Comparative Psychology.* Vol. 29, pages 401–60, 1940.
"Problems in the Biopsychology of Social Organization." T. C. Schneirla in *Journal of Abnormal and Social Psychology,* Vol. 41, pages 385–402, 1946.
The Social Insects. William Morton Wheeler. Harcourt, Brace & Co., 1928.

THE TERMITE AND THE CELL
May 1953

Our Enemy the Termite. T. E. Snyder. Comstock Publishing Co., 1948.

DARWIN'S FINCHES
April 1953

The Meaning of Evolution. George Gaylord Simpson. Yale University Press, New Haven, 1950.
Systematics and the Origin of Species. Ernst Mayr. Columbia University Press, 1942.
Darwin's Finches. David Lack. Cambridge University Press, 1947.

THE END OF THE MOAS
February 1954

The Moa-Hunter Period of Maori Culture. Roger Duff. Bulletin No. 1 of the Canterbury Museum. New Zealand Department of Internal Affairs, 1950.

THE METABOLISM OF HUMMINGBIRDS
January 1953

"Respiration and Metabolism." David W. Bishop in *Comparative Animal Physiology.* W. B. Saunders and Company, 1950.
Vital Energetics: A Study in Comparative Basal Metabolism. Francis G. Benedict. Publication No. 503 of the Carnegie Institution of Washington, 1938.

SHREWS
August 1954

"The Biology of the Smoky Shrew (Sorex Fumeus Fumeus Miller)." W. J. Hamilton, Jr. in *Zoologica,* Vol. 25, pages 473–492; December 31, 1940.
"On the Cause and Nature of a Poisonous Action Produced by the Bite of a Shrew Blarina Brevicauda." O. P. Pearson in *Journal of Mammalogy,* Vol. 23, pages 159–166; 1942.

THE DESERT RAT
July 1953

"The Water Economy of Desert Mammals." Bodil and Knut Schmidt-Nielsen in *The Scientific Monthly,* Vol. 69, No. 3; September, 1949.

BIRD AERODYNAMICS
April 1952

The Flight of Birds: Analyzed Through Slow-motion Photography. John H. Storer. Cranbrook Institute of Science Bulletin No. 28, 1948.

BIRDS AS FLYING MACHINES
March 1955

The Biology of Birds. J. A. Thompson. The Macmillan Company, 1923.

The Bird: Its Form and Function. C. W. Beebe. Henry Holt and Company, 1906.

Functional Anatomy of the Vertebrates. D. P. Quiring. McGraw-Hill Book Company, Inc., 1950.

A History of Birds. W. P. Pycraft. Methuen & Co., 1910.

THE NAVIGATION OF BIRDS
December 1948

The Migrations of American Birds. F. C. Lincoln. Doubleday, Doran, 1939.

SONAR IN BATS
August 1950

"The Avoidance of Obstacles by Flying Bats: Spallanzani's Ideas (1794) and Later Theories." Robert Galambos in *Isis,* Vol. 34, No. 94, Part 2, pages 132–140; 1942.

"The Sensory Basis of Obstacle Avoidance by Flying Bats." Donald R. Griffin and Robert Galambos in *Journal of Experimental Zoology,* Vol. 86, No. 3, pages 481–506; 1941.

SONAR IN BIRDS
March 1954

"Acoustic Orientation in the Oil Bird, Steatornis." Donald R. Griffin in *Proceedings of the National Academy of Sciences,* Vol. 39, No. 8, pages 884–893; August 15, 1953.

South America Called Them. Victor W. von Hagen. Alfred A. Knopf, Inc., 1945.

METAMORPHOSIS OF INSECTS
April 1950

General Endocrinology. C. D. Turner. W. B. Saunders Company, 1948.

"Researches on the Insect Metamorphosis." O. W. Tiegs in *Transactions of the Royal Society of South Australia,* Vol. 46, pages 319–527; 1922.

"Anatomy and Metamorphosis of the Apple Maggot." R. E. Snodgrass in *Journal of Agricultural Research,* Vol. 28, pages 1–36; 1924.

HORMONES IN THE ROACH
December 1951

"Endocrines in Invertebrates." Berta Scharrer in *Physiological Reviews,* Vol. 21, pages 383–409; July, 1941.

SPIDER WEBS AND DRUGS
December 1954

The Life of the Spider. J. Henri Fabre. Dodd, Mead and Company, 1913.
The Biology of Spiders. Theodore H. Savory. The Macmillan Company, 1928.

CONDITIONING AND THE EMOTIONS
January 1954

Lectures on Conditioned Reflexes: Twenty-five Years of Objective Study of the Higher Nervous Activity (Behavior) of Animals. Ivan Petrovich Pavlov. International Publishers, 1928–1941.
Adaptation. John Romano. Cornell University Press, 1950.
Feelings and Emotions. Edited by Martin Luther Reymert. McGraw-Hill Book Co., Inc., 1950.

CURIOSITY IN MONKEYS
February 1954

The Great Apes. Robert M. Yerkes and Ada W. Yerkes. Yale University Press, 1943.

THE YERKES LABORATORIES
February 1955

Chimpanzees: a Laboratory Colony. Robert M. Yerkes. Yale University Press, 1943.
The Ape in Our House. Cathy Hayes. Harper and Brothers, 1951.